CHARITY BEGINS AT HOME

With best wishes.
Michael Koe

Brigadier Michael R. Koe OBE

Magnolia Publications

ISBN 978-0-9560911-0-9

First Published in Great Britain by:

   Magnolia Publications, 2 Rectory Way, Wappenham, Towcester, NN12 8SQ, England.

Typeset in Perpetua 11 pt, and printed and bound by **Falcon Press**, Millbrook Close, St James Business Park, Northampton NN5 5JF, England.

CONTENTS

The Lord Coe, KBE (Seb)

FOREWORD

For those of us who have been touched by the unspeakable condition that is PSP, it is almost impossible to understate the impact that it has on victims and loved ones alike.

I lost my mother to the illness 3 years ago. She bore the last few months of her ordeal with an inhuman fortitude. Michael Koe experienced the same pathology over a decade earlier. Nobody who knows Michael will be at all surprised that from sadness he crafted a practical response. The PSP Association, his legacy to the memory of his beloved Sara, was designed to meet the two frustrations that all sufferers and particularly their families bear, namely that no-one has yet understood why it strikes and often leaves families in the caring role physically and mentally stretched to break-point. Research and practical support lay at the heart of Michael's vision.

This book chronicles the creation of the charity, which is of immeasurable help to anyone wishing to duplicate a similar project. It is well-researched, insightful and unique.

I am honoured to have been asked to write this foreword.

INTRODUCTION

Many books have been written about charities. Some seek to increase awareness of a particular charity's purpose. Others focus more on the writer's personal experience of working in the voluntary sector. This book is written by a rapidly ageing old soldier, whose four sons constantly remind him that his memory and even marbles are failing fast (perhaps excusing those inevitable errors of omission or commission in the book, for which I wholly take responsibility!) It covers a period of some sixteen years from when my lovely wife, Sara, then in her early fifties, was diagnosed as having a particularly devastating but then little known progressive neurodegenerative disease, Progressive Supranuclear Palsy, from which she died three years later.

The first chapter of the book is a personal one, describing the effect of this disease on our family and its progression to Sara's tragic death in 1995. The following two chapters outline the birth and growth of the charity that we set up together to help provide sadly lacking information and support for afflicted families, and to promote and sponsor research into its treatment and cure. The fourth, fifth and sixth chapters look at the three main objectives of the charity and our progress towards meeting them. The seventh covers the fundraising activities we undertook and the eighth outlines briefly the finances of the charity. The final chapter draws some conclusions and expresses thanks to the large number of amazingly generous supporters and friends from all walks of life, whose contributions enabled the charity to progress at such speed toward its objectives.

Progressive Supranuclear Palsy is the awkward name of this neurodegenerative brain disease; Progressive because it gets worse; Supranuclear because it affects the neurons in the brain in the basal ganglia just above the nuclei (controlling eye movement); and Palsy because it is a form of paralysis. The name is quite a mouthful and accordingly usually abbreviated to 'PSP'.

The book seeks to spread greater awareness of PSP both within the relevant medical profession and amongst the general public, so that the man on the street when asked what these sibilant initials mean, does not reply "I don't know" or "Play Station Portable". However, the core objectives of the book are to provide an archive history of the birth and growth of The PSP Association, to seek recognition of the work of those involved and to express thanks to all those whose generosity enabled us to fund this work. It has not been possible to include individual thanks to all those who have made donations to our cause over these years. They have been recognised in personal letters, in the newsletters and Annual Report and Accounts of the charity and in other ways, but without their support the work of The PSP Association simply would not have taken place.

The 'tale' told in this book brings us up to the Spring of 2008, with The PSP Association growing rapidly toward its objectives under its dynamic and purposeful new Chief Executive, Mrs Jane Hardy. The many families who suffer from PSP will hope, as I do, that in a few years time Jane will be able to write a follow up to this book on how PSP was conquered by the research that The PSP

Association, CurePSP and others have sponsored.

There are forty eight pages of illustrations and some two hundred photographs, each with a short caption in the limited space available. To avoid breaking up the text, these are not cross referenced to the text. The first sixteen pages of these illustrations cover my family's story and the setting up of the charity. The next sixteen pages of illustrations cover events that The PSP Association ran or took part in. The final sixteen pages are photographs of The PSP Association's Hierarchy, Trustees, Staff, Medical Advisory Panel and some of the other scientists, neurologists and technicians who carried out research sponsored by The PSP Association. In the pages and space available, some of the photographs are smaller than I would have liked and it was, with the limited space available, impossible to include a picture of everyone who consulted The PSP Association in its work or who took part in PSP related research. I would ask those so omitted please to forgive me!

I would like to finish with some grateful acknowledgements of those who have helped me in putting this book together. I am genuinely indebted for their encouragement and advice. Thanks must go first to The PSP Association and its staff, particularly Jane Hardy, who took over from me as Chief Executive in November 2007. Her encouragement and support have been fantastic. My thanks too go to Rebecca Benney, Director of Information at the Association, who has devoted many hours at home to editing drafts and to Debbie Benadie, who has spent many mornings in my house, at home and in the offices of the Association, helping to put the book together. Debbie's IT and secretarial skills were crucial to both its written content and its illustrations. I would like to thank all those medical professionals who have helped keep me on the right path in writing and editing this book, particularly its research chapter, though responsibility for its final wording and editing is mine alone. Professors Andrew Lees, David Burns, John Hardy and Dr Huw Morris all generously spent precious time in reading through and correcting my earlier drafts to bring them more in line with the latest scientific views of those concerned in such research. I am grateful to Mark Jordan, a friend of my son's, for his helpful editorial and publishing advice. I would also like to thank Tim Manderson, a local friend, whose long experience of publishing and contacts in the trade, helped me down the right road in the production of this book. Finally, may I collectively thank the many others who have encouraged and helped me to complete this book.

DEDICATION

I would like to dedicate this book to my lovely sadly late wife Sara, who seems nevertheless to be very much around, guiding our progress toward conquering this devastating disease.

SARA MARGARET KOE (née Stoneham)

1938-1995

LIST OF ILLUSTRATIONS

All photographs other than those from archives open to the public were printed from my family collection, from photographs previously published by The PSP Association in their Bulletin or, for some staff of the Association, taken by Debbie Benadie. Due to lack of space on the 48 photo pages abbreviated captions have been used. Full captions are below. The photos are not referenced in the book itself to avoid distracting the reader from the story.

Section 1. Photo Pages 1-16

Section 3. Photo Pages 32 -48

Heirarchy

Trustees

Staff

S3:p39_5.	Dr Angela Wilson	*Director of Medical Awareness and Research from 2007*
S3:p39_6.	Nigel Slater	*Fundraising Consultant 2005 - 2007*
S3:p40_1.	Maggie Rose	*Nurse Specialist from 1995*
S3:p40_2.	Tess Astbury	*Nurse Specialist 1999 - 2004*
S3:p40_3.	Grace Lewis	*Nurse Specialist 1999 - 2005*
S3:p40_4.	Cathy Magee	*Nurse Specialist 2006*
S3:p40_5.	Jill Lyons	*Nurse Specialist from 2007*
S3:p40_6.	Samantha Pavey	*Nurse Specialist from 2007*
S3:p41_1.	Caroline Clews	*Personal Assistant to the Chief Executive 1994 - 2002*
S3:p41_2.	Debbie Benadie	*Personal Assistant to the Chief Executive from 2002*
S3:p41_3.	Tricia Holmes	*Secretarial Consultant from 1995*
S3:p41_4.	Maureen Fowler	*Development Office East Midlands from 2005*
S3:p41_5.	Gina Rutterford	*Development Officer East Anglia from 2006*
S3:p41_6.	Sandra Campbell	*Development Officer Northern Ireland from 2006*
S3:p41_7.	Kathy Miller–Hunt	*Development Officer South West England from 2007*
S3:p41_8.	Michael Scott	*Development Officer West Midlands from 2006*
S3:p41_9.	Madeleine Quine	*Development Officer Scotland from 2007*
S3:p42_1.	Nichola Brookman	*Fundraising Officer 2001 - 2002*
S3:p42_2.	Jaine Colwell	*Support Backup and Events Consultant 2005 - 2007*
S3:p42_3.	Sarah O'Connor	*Events Coordinator 2005 - 2008*
S3:p42_4.	Bernie Herriot	*Support Back-up 2002 - 2003*
S3:p42_5.	Cameron Wood	*Fundraising Consultant 2003 - 2004*
S3:p42_6.	Cliff Davies	*PSP House Building Consultant from 2006*
S3:p42_7.	Alan Berry	*Trust & General Fundraiser from 2007*
S3:p42_8.	Lorraine Bowers	*Office & Care and Support Manager from 2007*
S3:p42_9.	Lis Nunn	*Events Coordinator from 2007*
S3:p42_10.	Jean Atkins	*Office Assistant 2004 - 2005*
S3:p42_11.	Elaine Elcoat	*Office Assistant 2006 - 2007*
S3:p42_12.	Lesley Wood	*Office Assistant 2003 - 2004*
S3:p42_13.	Sharron Arrowsmith	*Office Assistant 2004*

MEDICAL

S3:p43_1.	Professor Andrew Lees	*Chairman of The PSP Association Medical Advisory Panel (PSP MAP.) and Director, Sara Koe PSP Research Centre*
S3:p43_2.	Professor Lawrence Globe	*Deputy Chairman PSP MAP. and Chairman of CurePSP Medical Advisory Board. Consultant Neurologist, New Jersey, USA.*
S3:p43_3.	Professor Martin Rossor	*Member of PSP MAP. Consultant Neurologist, London.*
S3:p43_4.	Professor John Hardy	*Member of PSP MAP. Department of Molecular Neuroscience, London.*
S3:p43_5.	Professor Werner Poewe	*Member of PSP MAP. Consultant Neurologist, Germany.*
S3:p43_6.	Professor Yves Agid	*Member of PSP MAP. Consultant Neurologist, Paris.*
S3:p44_1.	Professor John Steele	*Honorary Member of PSP MAP. Consultant Neurologist, Guam.*
S3:p44_2.	Professor Eduardo Tolosa	*Member of PSP MAP. Consultant Neurologist, Spain.*
S3:p44_3.	Professor Irene Litvan	*Member of PSP MAP. Consultant Neurologist, Kentucky USA.*
S3:p44_4.	Professor Niall Quinn	*Member of PSP MAP. Consultant Neurologist, London.*
S3:p44_5.	Professor Nick Wood	*Member of PSP MAP. Director Department Molecular Neuroscience, London.*

1. *The reason why (Sara's story)*

The polished oak table glittered in the candle light setting of the Great Hall. Seated at the far end from me, Sara started crying. Our guests looked embarrassed. I walked down to comfort her. "The lights are hurting. They are too bright. I can't see properly." Taking her gently by the arm, I led her out of the room and slowly up the stairs, pulling on the carved oak banisters to help maintain our combined balance. Then, sitting on the bed, looking lovely but lost, Sara whispered, "Go back to our guests. I'm alright." But both she and I knew she wasn't.

It had all really started some six months earlier. After I had left the Army, we had moved up from our house in Fulham to South Northamptonshire, where we had fallen in love with and bought a beautiful old, but crumbling, Manor House. We had planned to spend the rest of our lives – and money – in restoring it to its former glory.

Built in 1540, but in early Elizabethan architecture[1], with mullioned windows and carved Hornton Stone architraves, it boasted a Great Hall, a Minstrel's Gallery, a panelled Drawing Room and a Solar, from which the ladies could admire or at least look down through an internal window at their men carousing in the Great Hall below.

Sara had been loading rubble in the corner of the Stables, when she had hit her head hard on a corner of scaffolding, knocking herself out; and inflicting, just above her right eye, a nasty cut. The Doctor put in a couple of stitches and we all expected her to be OK in a couple of weeks, but it didn't work out that way. Gradually and imperceptibly, a series of little concerns, like a slight unsteadiness, dislike of bright lights and tunnel vision, all hard to put your finger on, began to emerge and worry us.

Sara had been a stunningly attractive debutante in the 1950s (they still existed then and had much fun, as such!) and had at that time been a Secretary (very part time!) at the Post Graduate School of Medicine in Harley Street, living nearby in her Grandparents' apartment.

She had become interested in and knowledgeable about medicine and had, ever since, kept a small library of obscure reference books, through which she now pored, seeking to match her difficult-to-define symptoms. For, in addition to worries over her eyes and emerging problems in vertical gaze (she couldn't look up at the ceiling or down at the floor without moving her head), she had a growing fear of falling, sore eyes, a stiff neck and her handwriting had become tiny and cramped.

Meanwhile her GP appeared to be at a loss as to the cause. The ophthalmologist Sara was referred to could not detect anything basically wrong with her eyes. Then, worryingly, a CT scan revealed some shrinkage of parts of her brain; and we were questioned closely about her drinking habits. Sara hardly drank at all, but at that time some friends understandably – but unfairly – sus-

---

1. *Elizabeth came to throne 1556*

pected she was turning to the bottle (it was similarly assumed that Dudley Moore suffered from a drink problem before his diagnosis of PSP).

After some six months, Sara was referred to a neurologist, who did some tests and concluded that it was possible that she might have Parkinson's Disease, but would need to see her again in a few months time. Then, through one of our elder sons, Jamie, we were put in touch with a Dr (now Professor) Martin Rossor, an eminent Neurologist at the National Hospital for Neurology at Queen's Square in London, who asked Sara to spend a few days as an in-patient there, while he carried out further tests.

Over the next week, in the neurological ward in the Hospital, he and Dr (now Professor) Andrew Lees, another world-leading expert in this field, examined Sara. They carried out exhaustive tests, including – whilst I was there – some hilarious quiz games, like "How many animals can you think of beginning with the letter *C*?" Sara's 'Cobra' was rejected as not being an animal, much to her displeasure. She insisted that two went into the Ark together!

At the end of the week, Dr Rossor asked me to come to his office, as he said he had some concerning results, which he would like to discuss. Fearful – for I knew already that it was likely to be bad news – I went along. He looked overworked, under pressure and strained. He explained that there were no definitive tests in this area of neurology (except from post-mortem examination) absolutely to confirm a diagnosis such as he had made in Sara's case. However, the symptoms that he and Dr Lees had observed fitted his diagnosis; they both believed they knew the cause.

Dr Rossor and Dr Lees concluded that Sara had not Parkinson's Disease, but its 'ugly cousin', Progressive Supranuclear Palsy. Dr Rossor felt that the blow on Sara's head may just have been coincidental in timing with the onset of what he described as a neurodegenerative disease. He then said that there was still no effective treatment and no cure for this disease. He told me, I think, quite lot beside, before giving me a note asking for Sara to be readmitted for further checks six months later. I nodded politely, but my mind had turned inward and my world had just stopped. How would I break this half-expected but shocking news to Sara? She was intelligent and astute. She wouldn't easily be fobbed off. How would I tell our four sons?

Dr Rossor asked if I had any questions. I remained in stunned silence, grappling with what he had said. Reasonably assuming I had no questions, he explained he must go to other patients, but would see us again when I brought Sara back. I realised after he had left that there were so many questions I should have asked, but had been too shocked to think through clearly. In fact, I couldn't exactly remember all of what he had said.

I wished there was a nurse or someone who could talk me through what to do next and about Sara's care. Dr Rossor had said that PSP was progressive and affected balance, movement, vision (particularly upgaze and downgaze), speech and – at a later stage – swallowing. He had emphasised that it was a very individual disease and affected different people in different ways. Some people remained on a plateau for a long time. He said average life expectancy was some seven years from onset. When was that?

I understood that there was no effective treatment and no cure for this disease, but that there was ongoing research into its mechanisms. He had also mentioned Dr Irene Litvan, a leading scientist and neurologist in the USA was researching into oxidation and mitochondria, and their linkage to brain diseases. She had written a book on PSP (and later gave me a signed copy)[2].

Dr Rossor had emphasised that it was a very difficult disease to diagnose and that, in the lifetime of the patient, a neurologist was doing well if he or she achieved ninety percent accuracy against the gold standard (pathological examination), since any in vivo assessment had to be based entirely on symptoms observed. There was then and still is today no definite diagnostic marker, such as from a blood or spinal fluid sample, although brain scanning can now provide strong clues.

I clung to the hope of that ten percent – that the diagnosis was wrong and that Sara had something less life threatening. I knew she would want to know as much as possible, so in the car driving up the M40 back to home, I explained as best I could what I had been told, stressing that there was an element of doubt about the diagnosis and even if she did have PSP, what an individual disease it was. Her medical reference books didn't really help, so we discussed a visit to the USA to see if there was treatment over there; and perhaps to meet Dr Litvan.

Later that day, I broke the news to our three older sons. The elder two were working in London and our third was just finishing at Oxford. By the time I managed to contact our youngest, then at Edinburgh University, he had already heard the news on the family grapevine. All four tried to cheer me up.

"Dad, it will be all right – they've probably got the diagnosis wrong." "Mum's strong – she'll pull through."

"They'll find a cure soon."

"It's a very individual disease. It may just go away."

But I could tell that they, like me, were shattered by the news, though they had known for some while something was wrong with Mum.

Back home, things started to get worse. One morning, standing by our bed on the edge of the carpet, Sara suddenly and without warning fell backwards like a log. Twisting sideways, she struck her head on the edge of the bedpost and, with a sickening thud, the hard bare oak floor. The sheer unexpectedness of her fall was particularly shocking and frightened us both. As an immediate result, Sara lost a lot of blood and required six stitches in the back of her head. We put down extra carpeting and sought ways of making the house more 'fall proof'. On walks thereafter, she was constantly in fear of falling, particularly alongside the canal (one of our favourite routes) and needed me to put my arm around her as we walked. But walking for her was already becoming much more difficult.

Whilst my elder two sons Simon and Jamie (helped enthusiastically by the younger two, Richard

2. *PSP Clinical and Research Approaches, Edited by Irene Litvan MD and Yves Agid MD PhD 1992*

and Digby) looked after their Mum, I flew over to the USA to attend a Symposium for Carers of those with PSP at the John Hopkins University Hospital in Baltimore, where Dr Irene Litvan was speaking. The Symposium was organised and run by David Saks, whose wife Reba had PSP from which she sadly died in 1993. David himself died in September 1995, but not before he had founded the Society for PSP in Baltimore. He was a great motivator, a terrific organiser and a tireless worker, humble and honest to a fault. He was the driving force behind the US Society and Congressional lobby group and the inspiration for our own Association. Some thirty to forty of us attended his 1993 Symposium.

The scientific talks explained what research into PSP had been carried out thus far. There was an animated discussion about this, but it was clear that there was still a long way to go before any drugs to modify the progress of the disease might become available; although its basic mechanisms were beginning to be better understood.

Various drugs and therapeutic treatment were available on prescription to help with symptoms and in quality of life, but my hopes of some effective treatment or even a cure for Sara were dashed. It was, however, good to meet people 'in the same boat as us' and for me the first seedling of an idea to set up a similar group in the UK, along the lines of the embryonic US Society, was perhaps planted then. I returned to the UK with some new friends and useful contacts in the PSP field.

With no orthodox treatment available and months to wait to see Dr Rossor again, we felt we had to try something and there seemed nothing really to lose in exploring 'Alternative Medicines'. So we travelled, as politicians would say, up and down the country to try out friends' suggestions. It all started with our Lord Lieutenant's distinguished cousin, who had built up a reputation for curing people by 'laying on of hands'. He lived in a stately home to the north, close to Nottingham.

On our first visit, he explained his limitations but said he would be happy to have a go; inviting me to stay whilst he worked on Sara. His technique involved placing his hands on her head to 'draw out the disease'. This, he explained, drained him; and involved periodic hand washing to remove particles of the 'drawn out' disease'. Driving home, Sara admitted to feeling much better. However, after three visits, both she and he recognised he could not really help; the disease was too strong.

We next tried Acupuncture. We were both a bit nervous of all those needles but, in the event, parking in the centre of Oxford was, at least for me, more painful than the skin puncturing! As an observer, though, it looked a bit like a medieval torture technique. Once again, Sara felt better after a session. We also tried the special Chinese medicinal food they offered there, which I personally found disgusting, but Sara, who could then still swallow, quite liked, though it didn't seem to help much.

Once again, a couple of months later, there was still no sign of any genuine remission of the relentless progression of the disease, so we switched to having a go with a recommended faith healer, who lived in Bromley. It was a long drive from South Northamptonshire to Bromley, but we finally arrived at a small terraced house, in a difficult to find cul de sac.

We were met there by a middle aged lady, with a strong no-nonsense personality who invited us in and offered us a welcome cup of coffee and biscuits in her main living room. Wilson, our Staffordshire bull terrier had travelled down with us. He too was invited in and accepted, in a gentlemanly way, an offered biscuit, before lying on the carpet by the fire, head in paws and legs stretched out behind him. We then got down to business, describing to her what we knew about this little known but devastating disease. She listened patiently and then spoke about her previous successes with patients, where those offering orthodox medicine had effectively given up.

Rather nervously, we then obeyed her request for us both to face the fire and keep our gaze fixed on it, whilst she spoke in a melodiously accented monotone. We dutifully listened and then, as instructed, all meditated in silence, still looking at the fire. After five minutes of this meditation, I caught Sara's eye. Unseen by our hostess, she started to giggle. I did my best to keep a straight face, but was spotted. I was clearly not helping achieve the necessary level of concentration and was politely asked to take Wilson out for a walk in the nearby park, and to come back in an hour.

Wilson and I had a good walk. On my return with him, Sara was tired and keen to escape. We left, after thanking our hostess for her help and hospitality, and we said we would let her know about a further session when we got home. We drove back not knowing whether to laugh or cry. It had sadly not been the success we had hoped, but we felt to some degree that it was probably our fault. Sara was a lapsed but nonetheless strong Catholic, who had broken with the Pope over contraceptives and childbirth. Nearer the end, her faith was a tremendous strength in fighting this devastating disease, but with our Bromley healer it was, regrettably, like mine, lacking.

We next tried out a wide range of other 'touch' therapies and complementary medicines, including cranial osteopathy, reiki (a form of gentle Japanese spiritual therapy), reflexology, chiropractic, aromatherapy and even lead swinging. Some of these were, anyway, symptomatically helpful.

Alternative and complementary medicines are almost invariably offered without the backing of large scientifically controlled studies to prove their effectiveness. Their benefits are therefore more in the eye of the beholder and tend therefore to be reported through hearsay evidence. The orthodox medical professionals will also remind you that the 'placebo effect' of a completely inactive or bland therapy can be considerable, often leading to a perceived improvement.

Many alternative medicine practitioners tend to charge £20 to £30 a session, which, as we learnt, can add up. This is not normally covered by the NHS. Some practitioners I spoke to suggested that even if Sara was not actually getting better, she would have been getting worse faster, if she had not been given the treatment they were offering and, accordingly suggested we should continue to come to them for a longer course. We were also caught in the trap of not having enough time to try all the alternative medicines on offer (and we were unable to find any unbiased medical guidance on which therapy was considered by the author best for those with this particular neurological disease).

When, as a result, we took on more than one at a time, there was a further issue in deciding which, if either, was doing the job. Finally, travelling to where the practitioners lived became more and more difficult; so, reluctantly, we abandoned the alternative medicine route.

Sara's condition continued to deteriorate. Her balance, movement, speech and ability to swallow all worsened. At this stage, we were fortunate to find privately someone who would 'live in' and help look after her. Pam Adams, whose family then lived in Leicestershire, moved into the outbuilding, which we had initially converted from a hay loft into an art gallery and then into a small flat. She became a key member of our household, helping me with all aspects of looking after Sara over the next two years. It was Pam who looked after the house and Wilson, when we returned to London for our second appointment with Dr Rossor. At this, he was able to confirm that Sara had PSP and prescribed suitable drugs, including Amantadine and Prozac, the latter to help fight the depression which the disease, not surprisingly, inflicts.

Time and the disease moved relentlessly against us. As a family, we reluctantly and with sadness agreed that Gayton Manor, with its stone floors and stone steps, its different levels and its awkwardly located kitchen, was becoming impossible as a home for someone living with a progressive neurodegenerative disease like PSP. We all agreed that we really had no choice but to pack up and sell. After some heart searching and looking around, we found a much more suitable house only nine miles away in an attractive, small village enticingly called Wappenham. The village lies 16 miles south east of Northampton. The Old Rectory there, one of Gilbert Scott's first designs (his Father was Rector of Wappenham Parish), was up for sale and much more suited to Sara now. Accordingly, we put in a bid in the sealed-envelope 'shotgun' sale and were fortunate to have made the highest bid. We then sadly put Gayton Manor up for sale. Two months later, we found a purchaser and started to prepare for a move upon completion.

As time went by, Sara was finding swallowing increasingly difficult. Food needed to be pureed and water thickened. Even so, feeding and drinking became increasingly more difficult and more time consuming for her. Her pills had to be crushed and mixed in with mashed potatoes and the like. My cooking skills were stretched and, though Pam did a great job, Sara was by then, worryingly, losing weight. In July 1994, she was admitted to Northampton Hospice for a week's 'respite care'. This respite care is not so much for the patient – although it does mean they are looked after professionally for a few days – as to give the often exhausted carer a break. I could still visit her as long as I wanted each day and it was only a short drive away from Gayton. During this respite care, Sara began to hallucinate. She told me she was seeing strange crawly animals around her. She was frightened and I began to fear she was moving into a different world. That evening, I left her with reluctance to return to Gayton.

At about 9pm, back at home, I received an urgent call from the hospice. Sara was shouting and dementing; and could I come urgently. On my arrival some twenty minutes later, she did not recognise me and was fighting off the nurses, who were trying to restrain her. I held her down and actually lay on top of her until she relaxed, telling her repeatedly that it was all right; that there were no animals and if they came we would fight them off together. I don't think she understood a word I said, but she slowly quietened. She was then taken by ambulance, with me following by car, to Northampton General Hospital, where she was placed on a drip and treated for acute dehydration.

By the next day, she was much better, relaxed and peaceful and gave me a lovely smile in recognition. My heart felt broken, but gradually over the next month, her condition improved. Although her speech was difficult and slow, we had evolved a 'squeeze my hand' speaking code and were able to discuss, amongst other things, the question of PEG (Percutaneous Endoscopic Gastrostomy) feeding. This involves the insertion of a thin tube, which enables the recipient to be fed directly into their stomach, without taking food through their mouth. Where swallowing has deteriorated to the point that it is no longer possible to maintain adequate nutrition and hydration, and there is weight loss and increasing risk of chest infections and/or aspirational pneumonia, then this option needs considering.

There is probably no right or wrong decision around such issues. Some people with PSP find the PEG improves their quality of life and extends the duration of the disease. Others, especially if they have other serious symptoms and are at an advanced stage of the disease, may judge the potential benefits as not worth having. In Sara's case, we both agreed it definitely was worthwhile. So Sara came off the drip and had her PEG fitted. She remained in hospital for a further two weeks. I learnt how to help her with the feeding process; and that the system was much easier and more discrete than I had expected. I think Sara found the same.

She came back home two weeks later, tube fed, in a wheel chair, to our new home. My four sons, Pam and I had, whilst Sara was in hospital, packed up everything at Gayton, mainly in cardboard boxes. Unfortunately, in our distracted haste, we had failed to list the contents of some of them, which caused us much grief the other end. The removal men came three days before Sara was discharged, and we did our best to sort everything into our new home over that weekend. All the cardboard boxes were piled six high in eight rows in our fortunately large new dining room. Over the next few weeks we found ourselves rushing out to buy things we already had somewhere in one of the boxes, but needed urgently and couldn't find!

The box-laden dining room looked out onto the garden; so our beautiful old oak dining table had to be taken apart and lifted through one of its windows, which we had removed, so that it could be re-assembled in the already overcrowded room. Moving from a much larger house, with considerably larger rooms and higher ceilings, meant some arbitrary and tough decisions on what had to go. Thanks partially to our helpful and patient 'movers' and partially to the thirteen previous moves we had experienced over my Army career, we somehow coped. But it was many weeks before everything was unpacked and relocated; with some frustrating moments. All this was, of course, very secondary to Sara's deteriorating condition.

We had been fortunate with our GP and the multidisciplinary team he set up to support Sara at this advanced stage of her PSP. A very neat twenty first century vertical lift, which could take a wheel chair, had been fitted in or new house. It was electrically controlled and went up from the entrance hall to what we called the ironing room immediately above. The ground floor ceiling was quite high – some nine foot six inches above the floor. When the lift was down it had a 'hat' which formed the floor of the ironing room above, with a matching cut out piece of carpet on the top of the lift. When it was up, it had an underside, which matched the ceiling below and left the hall looking entirely normal. It had coloured flashing lights and buttons. We called it formally 'Dr Who's Lift' or just 'Who's lift'. You could push the chair in, shut the door, push the button and up it went. Sara rather wistfully whispered that she wished it would take her up and up to another, better world.

Our multi-disciplinary team included a dietician, who provided the liquid feed and advised on operating the kangaroo pump which gave Sara her calorific feeding requirements each day. The PEG, which tucked in on her stomach, was quite neat – just a thin coil of piping, which had to be connected to the pump. The actual feed took some time, but we could set it off to do its stuff at night. We used a cupboard in our bathroom to hold the bottles and other paraphernalia. A District Nurse came twice a day to check all was well and so we were very grateful for this new support. With the move over we had, sadly, to say goodbye to Pam, who needed to return to her family in the North of England. We both very much missed her. She had been a wonderful help and good friend to Sara and me.

Sara made a great effort to recover and much enjoyed her sessions with the Physiotherapist, whom she persuaded to help her try to walk again. With great effort, she managed a few tottery steps between us and never gave up trying. She also much enjoyed those crisp sunny November days, when she and I went out together, keeping mainly to pavements or paved footpaths, on our wheelchair walks. On one of these, going around a Wheelie bin on the pavement, I carelessly let the wheel of the chair go over the curb. Although I half caught her, Sara fell awkwardly onto the road and bruised and cut her cheek. She was very forgiving but I felt bitterly ashamed of my careless wheelchair driving and was much more careful thereafter.

The Speech and Language Therapist, who also came regularly, carried out a video swallow to check on Sara's by now rapidly declining ability to speak. She obtained for us a speech amplifier and we were visited by an IT technician, who looked at possible computer assisted communication programmes, including a sophisticated system which could, when you pressed the right buttons, open and close the curtains, turn on the television and lights and open doors. However, even the simpler ones, which displayed sentences on the screen, involved finger dexterity and control of eye movement, which Sara by then sadly lacked.

Communication had become very difficult. Sara's mind was as sharp as ever, but she could no longer write legibly nor could she speak other than in a difficult to understand guttural whisper. Before the speech amplifier and magnetic letter board had ceased to help, we worked out and used a communication system, based on 'squeeze my hand'. I would go through the alphabet and she would squeeze my hand when I had reached the right letter. This was painfully slow, but better than nothing; and I became surprisingly quick at guessing what she was trying to say. We also devised a communication 'code'.

When she squeezed my hand twice, we would use our code. This consisted of a page of useful statements, such as, "I am tired and want to lie down", "I am hungry", "I am cold" and, especially enjoyed by Sara, "shut up". Each statement had one letter of the alphabet. So after a double squeeze, I would recite the alphabet and at the right letter, she would squeeze my hand and I would read out the statement to be sure I had got it right!

On our next visit to Queen Square and the National Hospital, Dr Rossor felt an injection of Botulinum Toxin might help ease the stiffness in her neck, which was forcing her head backward. Botulinum Toxin is better known for its use in removing wrinkles, so Sara joked in her whisper about this being her beauty treatment! She was admitted to the hospital overnight and we drove back next day. She felt it had definitely helped and her neck was more comfortable.

Life, however, became increasingly more difficult as Christmas approached. Sara loved Christmas and in the past had done so much for all the family to make each one special. I was very aware I was not coping so well and at times the frustration and lack of sleep left me angry and in despair, but with no-one except Sara and our loving and gentlemanly Staffordshire Bull Terrier, Wilson, to take it out on. He gave us unconditional love, so I couldn't vent my frustration on him! One evening, in desperation and anger, I kicked out alternatively at a poof in one of the rooms to find out, very painfully, that it had a wooden bar concealed under the material, at shin level, which I struck! The next day, I was somewhat less than truthful when the District Nurse asked me why I was limping!

The night feeding, too, became more difficult and time consuming; and the relentless progression of the disease now involved spinal neurons, with consequent embarrassing incontinence, more night calls and emergency laundry. Helping move Sara to the bathroom was painfully slow, although a hoist, special mattress, grab rails and other gadgets had been provided. Health and safety rules prevented nurses and other helpers bodily lifting patients into a bath, although I continued to do so for Sara. Despite the PEG feed, she was continuing to lose weight and was surprisingly light now. Although we had a shower and put a seat therein, it was not an easy transfer and the bath was nicer.

I should stress, at this point, how fortunate we were with the help being provided. I was still trying to run our charity and was very aware of how little of the tremendous support we were receiving was being offered to many others in similar or worse circumstances than us. People were still being left to cope on their own, through failure in communications between them and the NHS system and Social Services, or even just appalling lack of such support. However, this realisation ashamedly did not prevent me from occasionally going into the garden to shout and off-load my frustration and despair. Sara was made of much sterner stuff and rarely, if ever, complained. She occasionally wept, but usually just smiled, laughed or just stoically sat in her imprisoning wheelchair. I could only imagine the pain and ignominy she went through, not least the humiliation of her growing incontinence, particularly for someone as fastidious and private as her. I can still remember vividly with shame the times I gave her less than the full support she needed. At this stage of a Carer's life, guilt and exhaustion loom large.

Christmas came and went. There were some happy moments, with all four boys with us. We took Sara for long walks in her chair and played childish games together, but both of us were aware that time was running out. By then she had signed up a Power of Attorney and discussed a living Will. Meanwhile little things like washing her feet or cleaning her teeth made a huge difference, she indicated, to her quality of her life.

On 20th January 1995, Sara could not sleep nor take in her feed from the kangaroo pump feed, without regurgitation. She needed to sit up, because of the concerning wheezing in her chest and difficulty in breathing. Neither of us slept much. As early as I dared, I rang our GP, who arranged an ambulance to take her to Northampton General Hospital. The ambulance arrived quite quickly and, using the lift down we transferred Sara in her wheelchair into the back of the ambulance. I then followed it by car to the hospital, where she was quickly examined and given an oxygen mask to help her breathing. After a couple of hours in Accident and Emergency, she was taken up to a private room off a ward. I stayed with her until around seven pm.

My son, Richard's graduation ceremony was to take place the following Saturday. He had been awarded a first in History at St Edmund Hall, Oxford. I was worried that Sara, who was very keen to be there, would not be well enough to make it, but still felt there was a good chance she would recover quickly enough. I waved her goodbye and drove back to Wappenham to greet Jamie who had driven up when he heard that she had been admitted to hospital. I told him she had aspirational pneumonia, but was on oxygen and in good safe hands. We decided therefore to visit again in the morning and sat up to watch a bit of a relaxing Bond movie. I went up to bed around 11pm. Soon after midnight, I had a call from the hospital. Sara had died.

Jamie and I drove on a cold, clear starlit night to Northampton and the hospital. We were escorted up to the private ward. Sara's body was lying there, but she had gone. I cut off a lock of hair and gently removed her wedding ring – then we left. I felt cold, empty, very tired and detached. We had been married thirty seven years. The future looked bleak.

2. *The setting up our charity and its challenges*

Progressive Supranuclear Palsy involves the progressive death of neurons (nerve endings) in the brain, mainly in the basal ganglia and brainstem, just above the nuclei (hence 'Supranuclear' being a key part of its name). These neurons control balance, movement, vision (particularly upgaze and downgaze), speech and ability to swallow. The cause is still not known. There is no effective treatment and no cure for this disease today. Average life expectancy is some seven years from onset, the last two of which are often spent wheelchair- or bed-bound, tube-fed, on twenty four hour care, unable to communicate with the world around, even though the intellect is usually left largely intact. This cold factual summary of this devastating disease describes what in human terms means the slow but inexorable loss of all those capabilities that make life worth living: a life trapped in a non performing body but with the intellect largely intact – some would say a living hell.

Because it is slow and insidious, it is often not possible to give a diagnosis until some three to four years into the disease, and sometimes a firm diagnosis can only be made after death. (Problems with the diagnosis of PSP are dealt with under research in Chapter Five).

PSP is a very individual disease, but early (often ill-defined) symptoms can include fear of falling, problems with balance, dislike of bright lights, tunnel vision, stiffness and the arching of the back of the neck. Difficulty with looking up at the ceiling or down at the floor without moving the head is symptomatic of its classic presentation. Unexpected falls, often backward, can be both frightening and damaging. Problems with speech and the ability to swallow usually follow later. Readers should note that other neurodegenerative diseases, strokes and temporary brain damage can cause similar symptoms.

Some fifty percent of the UK population carry the gene which gives susceptibility to PSP. However, something else, perhaps another genetic or more likely an environmental trigger is clearly needed to set off the disease. Recent research confirmed for PSP an incidence across the UK of some 5.3 per hundred thousand of population and a prevalence of some 6.4, meaning that there are at least 4000 living patients across the country. However, leading neurologists consider this figure to be seriously low. Taking account of the difficulties of diagnosis and the number of cases misdiagnosed or not diagnosed at all (particularly among the elderly) whilst alive, they quote up to 10,000 as a more realistic figure.

Even taking the lower figure, this means that PSP is at least as common and, most neurologists would agree, at least as nasty as its far better known and researched 'cousin', Motor Neurone Disease.

Earlier on in her illness, Sara and I both became angry and upset over the general lack of knowledge and apparent lack of interest in neurodegenerative diseases in general (and PSP in particular) amongst relevant health and welfare professionals. In our experience at that time, no-one seemed to know what to do and no-one really seemed to care. In hindsight, this view was unfair, but because the medical profession as a whole knew little or nothing about this disease and had no treatment to offer, their apparent lack of interest was almost certainly more to do with embarrassment than lack of concern. And those few who knew were too thin on the ground to be able to offer, across the UK, the considerable and wide ranging support needed.

People with PSP and their families badly needed an Association of their own to take up their cause, to help them fight for better care and support; for greater awareness and for appropriate funding for research into cause, treatment and eventual cure.

Up to then, such patients had been encouraged to join the Parkinson's Disease Society, who generously provided an umbrella group. Although the two diseases show some similar early symptoms and result in similar nursing and caring requirements, they are now recognised to be biologically, pathologically and clinically quite distinct and different.

Until the early sixties, when PSP was first described by Steele, Richardson and Olszewski, three Canadian neurologists, PSP and Parkinson's used to be considered just one disease. Even today, PSP remains grouped with and generally referred to within the medical profession as 'parkinsonism' or sometimes even *Parkinson's Plus*, the 'Plus' being a reminder that unfortunately it progresses more rapidly than Parkinson's Disease and remains, as yet, untreatable.

In 1993, I met Mary Baker who was just about to take over as Chief Executive of the Parkinson's Disease Society (PDS). Mary was – and is today – one of the most dynamic people I have ever met. She now chairs the European Brain Association and the European Federation of Neurological Alliances. She is both charming and immensely persuasive.

Mary made a flying visit to see us at Gayton, where we met and talked about Sara's and my plans to register an Association specifically to look after those with Progressive Supranuclear Palsy. I discussed with Mary, in some detail, the mechanics of the setting up of such an independent Association. She whole-heartedly supported our plan and generously agreed my request that those with PSP, who had joined the PDS, should be offered the option of switching from it to join us once we were set up and running.

Having set out the broad objectives of The PSP Association (described below in an account of our first Trustees Meeting), Sara and I soon realised we would need a considerable amount of help and support to take things forward. It was simply not possible to set up and run a Charity with worldwide aspirations with just two people, particularly with one fighting a devastating progressive neurological degenerative disease like PSP and the other trying to support and look after them. We had to involve many other people, but in doing so, balance what we and our new charity could afford to spend, and rely to a large extent, certainly in the early stages of its existence, on the generosity of friends and relations and others concerned.

Their generosity was inspirational. People just seemed to appear out of the woodwork and offer help when and where they were most needed. In an ideal world, those setting up a new charity should, of course, have adequate support and a clear blueprint before starting up to ensure that events unfold at least approximately to plan. For us, certainly at the beginning, it did not happen that way. It all just seemed to evolve and 'grow like topsy'.

After Sara's death, I felt, in an extraordinary but very real way, her presence and faith in the Charity's early growth. This was, at the time, really important for me. However outwardly determined and confident I was that we would succeed (confidence that something will happen won't guarantee that it does, but without this confidence, it almost certainly won't!), the 'why bother' and 'why me' syndromes lurked there, particularly during the darker hours of the night and on many occasions it would have been all too easy just to walk away. Encouragement from friends and family was also hugely important, but Sara's tenacity of purpose and faith in outcome remained a paramount ingredient of our progress.

With the help of some good and influential friends, including Michael Morris (later Lord Naseby), the then Conservative Member of Parliament for Northampton South, who became our Chairman, Michael Carleton-Smith, the Chief Executive of Marie Curie Cancer Care, who had served with me as a Royal Green Jacket, (and who was later knighted for Services to cancer relief), James Stanford, then Chief Executive of Leonard Cheshire, Bryan Pascoe, another Green Jacket friend, and Denis Palmer, whose wife Patricia had PSP, we were able quickly to form a powerful and effective group of 'founder' Trustees.

Trustees of a charity are volunteers and are recruited as such. Good ones are not easy to find. They need to have the appropriate experience and knowledge to take on what is an extremely important and onerous job for the charity concerned. They need to be prepared to give up precious time for indoctrination, training and executive committee meetings. They need to read themselves into the charity's work and digest the legal responsibilities they are taking on. They are not paid for any of this, other than for out of pocket expenses, not one penny of which has yet claimed by any of our Trustees! The Charity owes all of those who served or still serve as Trustees of The PSP Association a great deal. Those not mentioned above or who became Trustees subsequently, feature in later Chapters of this book.

Meanwhile, the Charity Commissioners continue, in the interests of transparency and public concern over the voluntary sector, to place on Trustees ever increasing legal, financial and moral responsibilities. A charity needs to be lucky to find sufficient high grade Trustees willingly and able to take on this burden. The rapid growth and success of The PSP Association comes in no small measure from our Trustees skills and experience. They have collectively made a huge and more than generous contribution to our work and it direction.

Nigel Jones, a good neighbour, good tennis player, good friend and then Solicitor working in Northampton, generously took on the drafting of our proposed charity's Memorandum and Article of Association[3] without charge, so that it could be registered as a company limited by guarantee. It was incorporated accordingly on 19th April 1994 and established under its Memorandum of Association, which laid down the objectives and powers of the company, governed under its Articles of Association.

The structure, governance, mission and objectives of the charity, registered as The Progressive Supranuclear Palsy [PSP-Europe] Association, were accordingly approved by Trustees; and on 27th April 1994, following the regulatory process, it was registered as such with the Charity Commissioners.

The information below about the November 2006 Charities Act, which is changing the legal status of charities, is taken from an article by Francesca Quint, Barrister, with her kind permission:

'The Act proposes changes in the above system to simplify registration. This Act contains provision for a new form of incorporated body, to be called a Charitable Incorporated Organisation (CIO), designed exclusively for charities. It will not suffer from the drawback of dual regulation as currently applies to charitable companies, but will otherwise have all their advantages, including limited liability for its members. A CIO will not be a company but it will be similar. It will have to have members and a written constitution, and members may either have no liability or limited liability. It will be created, incorporated and also registered as a charity simply by registration with the Charity Commission.

As with a charitable company, there will have to be provision in the Constitution for both members and trustees, but it will be possible for them to be the same people. The Charity Commission will be directly involved in the conversion of a charitable company, or unincorporated charity, into a CIO.[4]'

The Directors of The PSP Association, that is the people responsible under the charity's governing document for controlling the management and administration of the charity, are also known as Trustees for the purposes of current Charity Law and are referred to as such in this book, (although under the Company's Articles, they are, confusingly, known as Members of the Charity's Executive Committee). The charity is governed by this Committee, whose Members are elected to serve for a period of three years after which, if they wish, they can offer themselves for re-election for a further period at the next Annual General Meeting. The Executive Committee consists of a minimum of five and maximum of fifteen Members and the serving Chief Executive.

Immediately after registration, we set about seeking appropriately high-grade scientists from across the World to help form a Medical Advisory Panel, to guide the Executive Committee on research matters. Most of those who accepted then or later are now Professors and world renowned in their field; and all are highly respected neurologists in their respective countries.

Sara had been diagnosed as having PSP by Martin Rossor and Andrew Lees at the National Hospital for Neurology. The former was even then a world recognised expert in Alzheimer's Disease

---

3. *PSP Association Memorandum and Articles of Association.*

4. *Setting up a Charity – Professional solutions Charity Bill Update 14 Nov 06, Francesca Quint, Barrister, Radcliffe Chambers, Lincoln's Inn*

and the latter in Parkinson's Disease and PSP. Accordingly, we invited them both to be Members and Andrew Lees to be Chairman of our Panel. We also invited Professor Lawrence Golbe (then Chair of the Medical Advisory Board of the newly formed US Society for PSP) to be Vice Chair. His acceptance had an additional bonus in the coordination of US and UK research into PSP between the US Society and our Association, as Andrew Lees was Lawrence Golbe's deputy on the US Medical Advisory Board of the US Society for PSP.

We invited Irene Litvan and other eminent US and European neurologists and scientists to be Members of this Panel. We also invited, as an Honorary Member, Professor John Steele, one of the three doctors who had, in the early sixties, first described Progressive Supranuclear Palsy as a distinct phenotype or disease. We were delighted that they all accepted. This Panel, whose members feature in the books illustrations, performs a key role in the selection of research to be sponsored by our Association and the overall direction of our research endeavours.

In May 1994, we held our first Executive Committee Meeting at Marie Curie Cancer Care in smart offices in leafy Belgrave Square in Central London, courtesy of Sir Michael Carleton-Smith, their then Chief Executive. The Meeting was Chaired by Michael Morris (later Lord Naseby) and attended by all Trustees including Sara, who was still able to travel and speak. We each put £25 in the 'kitty' to start the charity off. It should be noted here that over the years, our Trustees have made other extremely generous financial contributions to the work of the Association.

An early agenda item debated at this Meeting was a controversial one. Even within the medical profession, there was considerable disagreement about the name of the disease. Some preferred 'Steele Richardson Olszewski Syndrome', some 'Richardson's Disease' and some 'Progressive Supranuclear Palsy' (either, as here, using capital first letters or spelled out, as in many medical references, in lower case). After some debate, the name opted for by the majority then present, was 'Progressive Supranuclear Palsy' or PSP for short, matching the nomenclature used by the US Society for PSP (since renamed 'CurePSP').

Our Charity had been initially registered as 'The Progressive Supranuclear Palsy [PSP Europe] Association' to reflect its European aspirations. It was decided, by a majority, to stick both to PSP as the name of the disease, as far as the Charity was concerned, and to keep on our letter head the full title used in the Charity's registration.

Despite our Charity Trustees' considered views, the disease itself still continues to be known around the world, by assorted variations of the above. However, the general public and vast majority of the medical profession now accept PSP as the authentic version of its name. Accordingly, in 2007, Trustees voted to simplify the name of the Charity to 'The PSP Association' and formally notified Companies House of this change.

Apart from settling the name of the Charity, we needed to agree precisely its Mission and Objectives. Selection and maintenance of the aim is a key principle of most human activities. The very straightforward and simple aim for The PSP Association, agreed by Trustees, was 'the conquest of

PSP', which, however, remains a task not so much for the Charity as for researchers researching across the World, not constrained by national boundaries. The Charity, of course, doesn't actually undertake research itself; in other words, we can only reach our goal of treatment and cure indirectly. Conquest in its literal sense will be by researchers, probably still some years ahead, based on an accumulation of previous work and knowledge within the worldwide scientific community.

In whichever country the breakthrough occurs, treatment and cure, if affordable, will become available worldwide, thereby achieving the Charity's goal. Meanwhile, close international cooperation is crucial for research to progress effectively to clinical trials and therapeutic treatments. Thanks to our own and the US International Medical Workshops and other meetings and fora, scientists involved in neurological research **do** work extremely closely together toward this common goal, often communicating on a daily basis by email and voice.

Our role in the provision of care, information and support to afflicted families and to health and welfare professionals is discussed further in Chapter 4. Across England and Northern Ireland, it is comparatively straightforward, though clearer direction from the Department of Health in England is needed as to whose responsibility is it to provide what information; and who is responsible for ensuring this information is appropriate and accurate. For the rest of the UK, the Charity works across different health regimes. Although these do not seriously affect its role, they do involve some necessary adjustment of information; and 'fighting different battles', for example in the provision of care.

Although our objectives were and still are broadly typical of most national medical charities, there was one awkward problem we had to address – our target audience. At the time, due to the then believed rarity and obscurity of Progressive Supranuclear Palsy, there was no other organisation except the European Parkinson's Disease Association (EPDA) willing and able to inform and support people with PSP across Europe. EPDA's overriding priority, not unnaturally, was for those with Parkinson's Disease rather than PSP. We therefore hoped to help in the setting up of other European PSP Associations and, accordingly, felt we should include in our objectives something about our European pretensions.

Across Europe, as described in more detail in Chapter Four, the Charity now cooperates closely on an equal basis with its French and German counterparts, having been involved in helping set them up on similar lines to ours. Elsewhere in Europe we provide support directly through our nurse specialists and our website or through the PSP 'branches', where they exist, of the European Parkinson's Disease networks

Outside Europe, we continue to work closely with CurePSP in the USA, with an informally agreed 'division of the world'. We respond, like them to worldwide queries about PSP (mainly coming through our website forum) and seek to support the establishment of similar PSP focussed organisations elsewhere in the World, as we have, for example, in Australia.

Raising awareness, too, has a worldwide component, but funding for this is inevitably limited and our focus has to be mainly the UK. Here, in addition to the need to raise awareness amongst the relevant health and welfare professionals and decision makers, there is a clear need to do so amongst those with influence and amongst the general public at large, since their support is crucial to the better services and to the essential funds we need to reach our agreed objectives.

From the above analysis, our key objectives listed below were agreed at our first Trustees Meeting and still stand today. They are to:

~ provide information and support to afflicted families across Europe
~ promote and sponsor research worldwide into the cause, effective treatment and eventual cure of PSP
~ engender awareness of this disease, particularly amongst relevant health and welfare professionals, mainly in the UK
~ fundraise to enable the charity to progress its other objectives.

At this meeting, promoting and sponsoring research was placed first, but all three were give equal priority and for the purposes of this book, information and support is addressed first; then research and then awareness.

Looking back to that time, these were remarkably challenging objectives for our new 'baby' and for those of us committed to make it all actually happen.

At our inaugural Meeting, we also concluded that we should be a subscription service; offering information, telephone counselling and local support groups in return for a modest subscription, which we would waive for those on income support or facing other recognised hardship. This subscription would enable us to keep track of those joining and provide the charity with a small but, particularly early on, important income. We would initially ask a modest £15 per year subscription across Europe. One consequence of this decision was that those who joined became subscribers, not members.

That meant that actual membership of the Association was limited to our Executive Committee. This limitation made it particularly important for us to involve and consult closely with our 'subscribers' – mainly afflicted families and carers – particularly in the selection of the way ahead. Since they were not technically members, they could not direct by vote decisions by Trustees.

In balancing allocation of funds between research, support and awareness, Trustees needed therefore to take particularly careful account of the views and wishes of carers and people with PSP – that is, the people the Association exists to serve and support. We needed to be seen, as far as possible, as a 'user led' organisation, despite the reality that people with PSP, as the disease advances, are in no position to 'lead' a charity, even a small charity such as ours.

Sitting at our kitchen table after our first Executive Committee Meeting, I was inwardly overwhelmed by what Sara and I had taken on and very concerned as to how we should actually implement our ambitious plans. I could hear, ringing in my ears, the remark of one of our more experienced Trustees, to the effect that the founder of any charity had a very lonely road to travel and needed, he said, looking me in the eye, considerable faith and determination to succeed. I felt he doubted I had that steely fibre he saw as necessary for success! I have to say I rather agreed with him and questioned my self discipline, application and other skills required to take the charity forward without Sara, whose faith and determination were, as her family well recognised, beyond dispute!

I remembered that we had agreed at our first Meeting only to hold our Trustees Meetings every six months, for that had seemed sensible at the time. For convenience, to fit our annual cycle, our Financial Year had been adjusted to run from 1st July to 30th June. (Now the Charity has 'grown up', there is a case to revert to the more normal tax year). Our Spring Meetings currently approve our budget for the following year and our Autumn Meetings receive the Charity's Report and Accounts, to be approved at the immediately following Annual General Meeting. I rather wished we had arranged to meet more often. However, those Trustees with experience of running charities were very understanding and helpful in responding to my many urgent telephone calls for help and guidance.

The PSP Association effectively started up in April 1994. Between then and 21st January 1995, when Sara died, my absolute priority had been her care and support. Over the next few months, as I struggled through the dreary administration and sorting of affairs in the aftermath of her death, with the necessary but petty round of activities that inevitably follow, I doubted I had the energy or enthusiasm to take the charity forward. I was too busy trying to regroup and redirect my life, though everything at the time, except for the heart warming condolence letters I received and wonderful support from my family and friends from around the World, seemed a huge effort and all rather pointless. My four sons were brilliant and a vital lifeline. Looking back, their visits (their duty roster up to Wappenham!) and support were largely what kept me going.

Amid this lack of direction and confusion, part of me was keen to get away from it all and move on to something different. Did I really want to continue this endless battle against an implacable disease and was I equipped to do so? But another part of me remembered the feeling of being abandoned by the 'system' and the perceived embarrassment of some of our friends, who thought Sara was perhaps on the bottle. I remembered also the doctors and nurses and those concerned in caring for her, who had so little in the way of treatment or even hope, at the time, to offer. I felt strongly that it was desperately wrong for people with this devastating disease not to receive the care and support that those with other similar diseases received from the NHS.

On a more personal note, I recognised the need to 'kick on'. You cannot go on just sitting around lamenting the past and moping over the future. If we were to move forward as planned at our Trustees Meeting, then it was time for me to get going and build a team; for, with the best will in the world, I could not run our new charity as a one man band, with Trustees Meetings once every six months. So I steeled myself to stick to the plan we had made to grow the charity to enable it to support others across Europe facing this disease. On cowardly reflection, this was an easier option than having to tell our other Trustees that I was not, after all, up to the job!

Before setting up The PSP Association, I had, for five years, run the Soldiers, Sailors and Airmen's Families Association (SSAFA) in Northamptonshire, where I was supported by, amongst others, John Greenaway (Sir John Greenaway Bt), who had also served as a regular officer, and who lived in the enchantingly named house called Lois Weedon in the village of Weedon Lois, the next village to Wappenham. John had generously taken on the role of Fundraising Organiser for SSAFA in Northamptonshire, so we had already worked together on a series of large fundraising events within the county.

He even more generously agreed to be, for an initial period, a Trustee and the Treasurer of our new charity. Brian Fisher, another friend, who also lived locally, and whose father-in-law had PSP, kindly agreed to become our Hon. Secretary and a Trustee so we now had an 'inner' team of three and we were on the march! We could start to look for our best route toward our given objectives.

Immediately after our first Meeting, the Charity's income was £300, thanks to the £25 per head donated by our Trustees, though soon to be swelled by subscriptions and donations from those joining our new Association. Based at the kitchen table, initially at Gayton and then in Wappenham – where Caroline Clews became the fourth member of our PSP Team – we now had Chief Executive, a Treasurer, an Hon Secretary and real part-time Secretary!

Caroline initially arrived for an interview at the Old Rectory, in Wappenham, just as the removals van from Gayton appeared, so her first job (she afterwards said she though it was perhaps part of my interview technique!) was to help me and the removers unload furniture and advise on where to put it in our new house, as Sara was then still in the Northampton General Hospital.

Caroline and her husband, David, were, at the time, building what was to become their future home in nearby Moreton Pinkney, on an attractive piece of land, on the edge of the village, which soon also housed a field full of their geese, sheep and horses. Caroline would bring along to Wappenham her very small daughter, Jessica, in a carry cot, and put her on the table, happily sleeping, whilst we struggled with the rapidly increasing requirements of the new charity, which was also starting to grow fast.

Caroline was remarkably efficient, a wonderful supporter and, unlike me, computer literate. With the generous help of a good friend of hers, Kate Lingard, who was a high grade and impressive IT Consultant, also living in Moreton Pinkney, we were also able to set up a very impressive patient and carer database, crucial to the continued growth of our work, at no cost to the Charity.

To complete our initial team, we were fortunate to find, initially as a volunteer, but later as a paid member, Peter Cover, who took on the task of setting up and running our Local Support Groups around the UK. Peter was a big man in every way, with a larger than life character and great sense of both humour and justice (later becoming a Justice of the Peace). He had been a Director of Sales at Milton Keynes for Audi Volkswagen and had 'the gift of the gab' as well as great compassion. He became our first Director of Care and Support, though we were still too small at this time to adopt such a high sounding title.

Soon thereafter, we recruited Maggie Rose, our first Nurse Specialist. She, her husband, Joe, and their family lived at the time in Gayton, where Sara and I had met them and they had become good friends of ours. Michael Carleton-Smith had recommended that we copy Marie Curie and set up for our subscribers a telephone counselling service, on a 24 hour answer-phone basis. We advertised accordingly and Maggie, already a fully qualified RGN, was our first applicant, whom we were delighted to take on! She joined us as a consultant and worked her own often very long hours. She is still a mainstay of The PSP Association at the heart of its work and has done, and still does, a wonderful job!

The National Health Service still tends to run a 'nine to five' service; and carers of people with PSP, who were by then joining our Association in increasing numbers, often worked similar hours themselves, so really appreciated the ability to telephone for help and advice about PSP 'out of hours'. Maggie took calls or responded to answer phone messages at any time of the day or night. Some were just to ask simple questions. Some were long and stressful calls from desperate carers. Others were sometimes just for a chat or a cry for help. Many of those who called, subsequently, often in moving letters, expressed immense gratitude for the 'lifeline' she provide for those often desperate for urgent help and advice, simply not available in unsocial hours through the NHS, except in recognised emergencies.

Before going further into our Charity's organisation, work and growth, it might be helpful to outline some of the challenges that neurodegenerative diseases and neurology in general pose; and, in more detail, those raised by PSP.

In 2001, The Neurological Alliance assembled the most authentic figures available then of the numbers of people affected by a neurological condition within the UK. Their best estimate was some ten million, which meant one in six of the UK population; and rising. These accounted for some twenty percent of hospital admissions and remain the third most common reason for seeing a GP. An estimated 350,000 people across the UK need help in daily living, because of a neurological condition, and over 850,000 people care for someone with such a condition yet Neurology remained the Cinderella of medicine.

There are a large number of different neurological conditions. The 'nastier' ones include those involving the progressive death of neurons in the brain (the closely related neurodegenerative diseases, which include Alzheimer's, Parkinson's and Motor Neurone Disease). Many have abstruse medical sounding names like Cortico Basal Degeneration, Multiple System Atrophy or Progressive Supranuclear Palsy. Most of these tend to be little known outside the specialist medical world.

One reason for this is that there is no simple, easy to trip-off-the-tongue collective name covering them all. The better known ones remain known individually by their given name, often honouring the scientist who first described them, rather than being known as a progressive neurological condition. Inevitably this limits public awareness of the others. Compare this to cancerous conditions. These, with all their many variations, are well known and feared by the public, collectively, as

'Cancer'. Perhaps a collective name such as '*Neurosy*' might attract greater public awareness collectively of these neurodegenerative diseases. For those concerned meanwhile, there is an important and challenging need to engender greater awareness of all these diseases, both individually and collectively, not just amongst the public at large, but within the relevant health and welfare professionals.

Those with such neurodegenerative diseases and their families and carers in particular, face many desperately daunting hurdles. In 1995, there was – and sadly even today remains – an appalling lack of information about what support is available through the State and from the National Health Service for those with such diseases, and even where to look for it.

For PSP sufferers, their journey from onset to death is still only too often truly horrific. With an average life expectancy of seven years from onset, it is often only after three to four years struggling with ill-defined but alarming symptoms, that someone with this disease can expect, if they are lucky, correct diagnosis. Thirty percent of these who join The PSP Association have been misdiagnosed initially as having Parkinson's Disease or another neurodegenerative disease or a stroke. And upon diagnosis, the overworked neurologist has too little time per patient. And rarely is there a Nurse Specialist to talk gently through the implications with the patient and their family or help look after the sufferer.

In the USA, there are proportionally at least four times the number of neurologists per head that there are across the UK, which, despite recent improvements, still lies near the bottom of the league in this respect across Europe. Regrettably, despite the promises of the National Framework for Long Term Medical Conditions, there is still a serious shortage (and a 'postcode lottery') in the availability of therapists and nurses needed to make up a multi disciplinary team to care for those with such diseases.

Many Care and Nursing Homes are unaware of the implications of having patients with a progressive neurological disease like PSP, and PSP patients are often treated as if they have dementia, though their intellect usually remains largely intact throughout the progression of the disease. Access to Palliative Care is now being addressed but this hugely important care in the later stages of such diseases is still only open to a lucky few. In default of this, several patients with Motor Neurone Disease (MND) or PSP across the UK have opted for the stark alternative of going to Switzerland for assisted euthanasia. Sadly, affected patients will continue to do so, at least until far better care and support is made available to all.

In 2001, some major improvements in this respect seemed to be just around the corner in the UK. Following an announcement of a new National Service Framework (NSF) for Long Term Medical Conditions in 2001 by Alan Milburn, the then Secretary of State for Health, and the decision later that year that this NSF would have a particular focus on Neurological Conditions, a list of Quality Requirements (QRs) were drawn up, with wide consultation across the voluntary sector.

However, it was not until March 2005 that these QRs were finally approved and announced by

Stephen Ladyman, then Minister for Health. (Some of those involved at the time, like me, felt that they could have been drawn up on the back of an envelope in a couple of hours. Most agreed that some consultation was necessary, though the four years actually taken before even looking into implementation was seen by the more cynical as delaying tactics to save costs!). There would, of course, be variations in the NSF's implementation across the UK, since following devolution, Scotland and Wales opted for different care planning within the NHS.

However, those concerned with progressive neurological conditions, like PSP, were delighted with the content of Stephen Ladyman's announcement and agreed that if these Quality Requirements could be implemented, this would result in a massive turnaround and improvement across the hitherto neglected neurological field.

The Minister went out of his way to make it clear that all Primary Care Trusts (PCTs) would have to comply with this NSF, with rapidly progressing conditions, such as PSP, specifically identified in several of the QRs, which were, to quote the Minister, "designed to put the individual at the heart of care and to provide a service that was efficient, supportive and appropriate at every stage from diagnosis to end of life". These were fine words indeed and music to the ears of those who struggled with the sometimes appalling lack of care and support hitherto provided; but there was some worrying 'small print'.

The Government opted for a decentralised executive process. Having laid out the policy and provided a major increase in overall health funding, the responsibility for the actual implementation of the NSF was to be delegated to Primary Care Trusts (PCTs), overseen by Health Commissioners. They had ten years in which to complete the implementation. No ring fenced money would be made available; "They already have had the money", said the Minister. Priorities in implementation would be set by PCTs, with Health and Social Care Commissioners responsible for oversight of progress in implementation. Three years on, decentralisation and delegation continue to be the buzz words but progress in implementation, or even a monitoring policy, is difficult to discern. Voluntary organisations within this Sector have been campaigning hard and will continue to do so, seeking genuine commitment to implement the NSF.

Commissioning of this NSF – and recognition of its primary focus on neurology – is crucial if, over the remaining seven of the ten years, Stephen Ladyman's fine words are to be translated into addressing the real needs of, and effective care and support for, neurological patients. Sadly, The PSP Association, and those other organisations supporting other neurodegenerative diseases, still regularly receives complaints of unacceptable neglect, lack of effective care and support, and ignorance from the health and welfare services, from patients with these diseases and their carers across the country; the very issues the QRs were designed to address.

A recent paper, by the Motor Neurone Disease Association on Care Pathway commissioning, indicated a cost of approaching £200,000 across health and social care of a patient with MND over their last year of life. Recent research confirmed a prevalence of PSP of at least that of MND and the care requirements are remarkably similar. The cost of care of a PSP patient in their last year of life is being currently assessed[5] in research into palliative care for such patients and patients with related rapidly progressive diseases. At the time of writing, this cost is not yet published, but there is no reason to expect it to be dissimilar.

The overall cost of care and support for those with progressive neurological conditions continues to raise many difficult and awkward issues. In Scotland, both care and nursing care are paid for by the State. In Wales, there are no prescription charges. In England, nursing care is paid for by the State but other care is paid for by the patient, on a means tested basis (although there is no logical or clear line between care and nursing care, so this division is pretty arbitrary).

In what is called 'Continuing Care', the Health Service in England and Wales takes full financial responsibility through PCTs for the overall care, in the later stages (whether at home, hospital or a nursing/care home) of selected patients, including those with PSP. Continuing Care is only on offer in England and Wales in defined cases, effectively in the terminal stages of the disease. However, because of cases where the Courts have found against the Government, the procedures as to whether and when to award this have recently been reviewed to seek to provide a fairer, more uniform system. Assessments are only as good as the assessors and their interpretation of the criteria on which decisions are based. Cynics suspect availability of funds continues to influence such decisions by cash strapped PCTs and cite examples which indicate that it pays to 'make a noise'. For there is an appeal system and those families who appeal and make a fuss often appear to succeed.

The above challenges of neurology provided a backdrop to the setting up and organisation of our new Association. How best should we 'fit in' and how should we address the considerable workload that such aims and objectives would demand? What should be our organisation? How should we seek it to grow? The next Chapter seeks to address some of these questions.

---

5. *Palliative Care in PSP and MSA sponsored by the DoH by Professor Nigel Leigh*

3. *Organisation and growth*

Our charity, The PSP Association, was now registered and, we hoped, poised to grow. We had our Trustees on board, we had an outstanding Medical Advisory Panel, we had a small team and we had a clear aim and clear objectives to achieve. This Chapter is about our early organisation and growth.

Sara's Memorial Service took place on a beautiful, sunny Spring Day on Saturday, 8th April 2005. It was held in the lovely old Church of St Mary's, Wappenham, just next to our house, where my sons and I held a reception afterwards. At the Service, Royal Green Jacket buglers played the moving 'High on the Hill' and my four sons, Simon, Jamie, Richard and Digby, each gave a short reading, including one about some of our highly competitive family tennis fours, with Sara almost invariably on the winning side.

Attractive, intelligent, vivacious and fun, she had been a brilliant hostess and legendary cook, with a special eye for Christmas and Easter celebrations, including painting 'happy faces' on our boiled eggs. Apart from her renowned tennis and tapestry skills, she also almost always won our many games of Trivial Pursuit, much to the annoyance of her husband and other members of her family. She had, too, been the driving force behind many of our family decisions, including the idea of setting up The PSP Association, of which she had become a founder member and Trustee.

At our May Meeting that year, Trustees felt it appropriate to select 8th April as the charity's Remembrance or 'Magnolia Day', with Sara's favourite flower, The Magnolia Grandiflora, as our Emblem. We informed the Charity Commissioners accordingly. Since then, courtesy of Peter Buckley, Chairman of the National Horticultural Society, whose daughter, Rosie, is a family friend, a Sara Koe Magnolia Grandiflora has been named and is currently being grown.

We now needed to raise the profile of PSP and our Association and draw public attention to this devastating and fatal disease; and we needed the support of people in the public eye to help us do this.

However, it was not until early the following Spring that, somewhat brazenly, I telephoned Sebastian Coe (now Lord Coe KBE), who had trained near us in Fulham, when we had lived there, to ask him if he would join my four sons outside the House of Commons one afternoon before the 1996 London Marathon for a photo shoot opportunity. I explained the reason why they were running and he, somewhat surprised by my 'cheeky' call, generously agreed. PR photos of Seb and my sons doing press ups immediately outside the Houses of Parliament – with, I have to say, some curious onlookers – were accordingly taken. Seb also generously agreed to become President of our Marathon Committee and sign letters I would draft to those who successfully completed marathons for our Charity.

It was a singularly extraordinary, improbable and unkind coincidence that some seven years later, his Mother was diagnosed as having PSP. "I couldn't believe it at first", he said "but at least I knew who to turn to for the support and information my Mother needed". Tragically, she died the evening he flew to Singapore to hear that London had been selected as the venue of the 2012 Olympic Games. Lord Coe, deeply affected by this family tragedy, was to play a very significant role in the later growth of The PSP Association.

As the Association grew, we also sought to enlist a high profile President and Patron to strengthen further awareness of the disease and of our Association. I had known Field Marshal The Lord Bramall, KG, GCB, OBE, MC as a serving officer of the Royal Green Jackets. He was now Lord Lieutenant of London. I invited him to become our President, with a minimum commitment, which, despite his heavy engagement schedule, he generously accepted.

We also held, in April 1996, an initial Reception at Grosvenor House in Park Lane, to which we invited HRH The Duchess of Gloucester, GCVO, as well as our new President, who both graciously accepted, after Lord Bramall had, we suspected, put in a good word for us!.

This was our first major charity event, and combined a champagne and canapés reception with an Art Exhibition for our growing number of friends. Having arrived half an hour before our distinguished guests, I was enormously embarrassed to find the zip on my trousers was stuck open! However the management of Grosvenor House were well up to such little problems and I was taken to a small room and asked to lie on a table, whilst one of the female staff sewed the two halves together, with me shrinking, as it were, inside! Decently dressed, I hurried down to the entrance in the nick of time to join the reception line for HRH's arrival!

Christopher Miers RBA, had been, for a short period, one of my Platoon Commanders with the 1st Battalion, The Royal Green Jackets in Borneo and as such was responsible for the successful defence of one of our more unlikely outposts, Bucket Knuckle, in Sarawak, against a probing attack by an Indonesian patrol. During this engagement our 105mm Pack Howitzer team, manned by an Australian crew, fired three rounds at some 100 yards range at the attackers. They claimed this to be the first use of this weapon over open sights since the Second World War. It was certainly a contender for the closest range! There were no casualties to the platoon and none admitted by the Indonesians, though some small white objects claimed to be bone from teeth were found near where the shells had struck! After this incident, the press, including Jak, the cartoonist, visited the site to produce a cartoon unkindly defaming our next door neighbours, the Royal Irish Rangers.

Christopher had later, after this tour, served with me again in Cyprus, then left the Army to become an artist; and by 1996 was already holding regular exhibitions of his work in London. He generously offered to exhibit some of his paintings and give the bulk of any sales at our Grosvenor House Reception to The PSP Association. Including donations from sales of his pictures, the Charity raised over £10,000 from this one event; a very large sum at that stage of our growth.

We then submitted an optimistic follow up request to Kensington Palace to invite HRH The Duchess of Gloucester GCVO to be our Patron. In light of our size and limited track record, this was, unsurprisingly at that stage in our growth, gently declined, but we were informed that HRH wished to continue to take an interest in our work and would be happy to support the occasional major fundraising function we might hold on an 'if available' basis.

On the strength of this response, we decided to reserve the position of Patron for her in the hope that, with continued growth, we could justify a further request. Meanwhile, the then British Ambassadors of France and Germany, respectively Sir Christopher Mallaby, GCVO, KCMG and Sir Nigel Broomfield KCMG (who both knew Sara) agreed to be our European Patrons, supporting our Pan-European aspirations. Soon thereafter, we were awarded £3,500 by the European Commission (to match our own expenditure in a pump priming exercise to help set up affiliated PSP Associations in Europe).

A year later, in July 1997, we were delighted to hear that HRH had graciously agreed to become our Patron and would attend, that Autumn, our Symposium for Carers and Therapists in London. Soon thereafter, we also learnt that Michael Morris, having retired as Speaker in the House of Commons, had been honoured as a Life Peer and had become Lord Naseby. The Charity now had a powerful, attractive and interested Royal Patron, a highly distinguished President, a popular and well known Vice President and a recently honoured and noble Chairman. Such impressive hierarchy could only enhance awareness of our charity and its work. And so it proved!

By now, the kitchen table in the Old Rectory was bursting at its seams and was no longer fit for purpose, with little room left, for example, for essentials, like breakfast, to be separated from the growing number of the Charity's paperwork and files!

Fortunately, the Old Rectory's outbuildings were eminently suitable for conversion into office space so, with the help of Christopher Hobson, a friend who ran a nearby architectural practice (and who was later to help us in our search for still more room in rented or bought accommodation, as the charity grew and as our outbuildings consequently became, over the years, also too small to fit our increasing numbers. He and his staff were to be immensely supportive to our fast growing Association, over the next decade). Under his supervision, builders were brought in to carry out the necessary conversion and we were able to move in to these newly converted rent free offices, courtesy of the Koe Family Trust. Our new (well mostly second hand) furniture was generously funded by our local Nat West Bank.

Meanwhile, John Greenaway was increasingly finding running his farm, looking after his family and meeting his many other commitments, whilst remaining our Treasurer, as our funds swelled and hours of work increased, just too much. He felt he must resign but had managed to persuade a friend of his, Gerald Kirby, whose career had been in banking, to take over from him as our Treasurer and as a Trustee. John had been a tremendous supporter and friend in the early days of the charity and I was very sorry to see him go and particularly grateful for his generosity in supporting us over the first difficult years.

Soon thereafter, we were shocked by the sudden death of one of our Trustees, our Honorary

Secretary, Brian Fisher, from a heart attack. He had been ill for several weeks, but this was totally out of the blue. His son in law, a Chartered Accountant, Peter Glithero, and another near neighbour, Joanna Tomkinson, generously offered to join us as new Trustees.

As we moved the now more formal charity into the Old Rectory Outbuildings, Joanna generously became our Honorary Secretary (slightly reluctantly in that role, I sensed!) for the next two years and Peter Glithero our Treasurer. Both Gerald and I resigned as Trustees, so that I could become a full time – and paid – Chief Executive and Gerald could be my Deputy and Financial Controller. In effect, we now both reported to the Board of Trustees as employees of the Charity. At the time, this was a difficult decision for me to make, involving 'the handing over' of what had become 'my baby' to other Trustees and becoming a paid employee, so that I could retain the day to day leadership of the charity's progress, full time, with a modest income to cover some of my living expenses.

At an early stage of the growth of The PSP Association, we recognised the need to recruit a fundraising specialist to help us handle appeals. We needed at this stage to find someone with sufficient experience, enthusiasm and skill to develop this vital side of our work. Sarah Wollaston, who lived near Peterborough and had worked for several years as a donor trust fundraiser with the 'Cot Death' Charity, came for interview with, in a push chair, her then small daughter Florence.

Sarah was knowledgeable, enthusiastic, likeable, intelligent and clearly extremely competent. She would initially work as a part time consultant from home. We felt we were very fortunate to find her and soon were sending out many successful appeals (which she drafted and sent to me to sign) for funding toward our projects, whether to sponsor research, raise awareness, produce information or to cover the costs of consultants or employees.

We also found the enormously capable and likeable Tricia Holmes. She lived in the next village and knew everyone. She already worked for several people including an Estate Agent in Towcester, and kept the books for her husband's building firm. However, she offered to help us out on a temporary basis as a consultant for a couple of weeks doing secretarial work, as Caroline Clews could only manage three mornings a week, and the workload was mounting. Eight years later, Tricia was still helping us out both in secretarial work and standing in for Gerald when he was on holiday! We have been extremely lucky to have her as 'back up'; and her son, Andy, also supported the Charity, over the years, as a highly skilled computer operator/analyst even as a teenager. He helped us, on an 'as and when' basis, to sort out our IT crises, until he left home for University, when we took on Mark Holliday, a cheerful, capable and professional consultant to advise and implement our increasingly ambitious IT plans.

When Caroline learnt that she was carrying her second child, she realised she could no longer commit to the growing hours the charity and I were demanding from my PA, so very sadly gave in her notice. She would keep in touch and help whenever she could, a promise she has faithfully kept. She had done a fantastic job and I was personally very sad to have to let her go.

Following a local advertisement, we interviewed several possible successors, including Debbie

Benadie, who had just moved back to England from Zimbabwe with her young family, and was living in nearby Brackley. She was bright, quick, capable, likeable and reliable; and handled pressure and demands coolly and calmly. She had a strong faith and lovely family; and, as a happy bonus, was extremely computer literate, with all the qualities to be an outstanding PA. I was absolutely delighted when she accepted the post, despite the modest pay and a competitive offer!

About a year prior to this, we sought help in running our fundraising events and brought in, through local newspaper advertisements a large number of potential recruits, from whom we chose Rebecca Bird, as a part time consultant and, four years later, as the workload grew, Sarah O'Connor, also on a part time basis, particularly to help in handling our increasing involvement in the London Marathon and other events, where we were building up our numbers participating as described later. Both proved to be hard working, capable and likeable operators; and both, later, became employees as crucial members of our growing team. A year after Sarah arrived, Rebecca (who had then married and changed her name to Rebecca Benney) left us to have a baby, but, fortunately for us, returned six months later, as our new Director of Information and PR (See Chapter 6).

After eight years as President of The PSP Association, our country's foremost soldier, Field Marshal The Lord Bramall, needed to reduce his heavy workload and wide ranging commitments and reluctantly explained he would wish to stand down on 30th June 2004, at the end of our financial year. This was a sad day and end of an era for our Association. Lord Bramall, throughout his long and distinguished career, had always done much more than just honour any commitment and had been a powerful President and generous supporter of our charity since taking up the post. A personal letter was sent him thanking him for all his work on our behalf, during his time in post; and for his many visits and appearances at our events. Lord Bramall responded:

"Dear Friends,

I have been so very proud to be President of The PSP Association for the last eight years and, now that I will fairly shortly, in June, be handing over to my successor. I wanted to take this opportunity to wish the Association and all who work for and with it all possible good wishes and continued progress in the year ahead.

As we all know, Progressive Supranuclear Palsy is a terrible debilitating illness, which deeply affects sufferers and their dependants alike. Yet it is quite remarkable what the Association has achieved over the last few years, under Michael Koe's inspiring and devoted leadership, to widen knowledge and understanding of PSP; relieve suffering of patients and dependants; and set research on the path of alleviation and, hopefully, one day a cure.

My wife Avril and I have met so many wonderful people over the course of these eight years, and it has been such a privilege to be associated with you in your great endeavours.

Yours sincerely,

Dwin Bramall"

Whilst serving in Germany, I had met Charles Guthrie, then a Welsh Guardsman and an 'up and coming' Brigade Commander. Several years later, in 2004, he had just completed an extended tour as Chief of Defence Staff. Having spoken to Lord Bramall, I optimistically wrote to him to ask if he would consider becoming our President, as Lord Bramall was retiring from the post. I did emphasise that the post of being our President was intended to be largely honorary and not too onerous. He generously accepted and, like Lord Bramall has been immensely encouraging and supportive to our cause; including, amongst his many commitments, attending a Trustees Meeting, a briefing at the Sara Koe PSP Research Centre, reading a lesson at the last two of our Carol Services and coming to one of our Windsor Race Evenings!

General The Lord Guthrie of Craigiebank GCB LVO OBE, President of The PSP Association, introduced himself to our Association below:

"Dear Readers,

I was delighted to accept earlier this year Michael Koe's invitation to take over as President of the Progressive Supranuclear Palsy (PSP) Association from my distinguished predecessor, Lord Bramall, on his retirement on 30th June; and would like to continue in 'his footsteps' as a strong supporter of your Charity and of PSP afflicted families. I am very aware of his 'legacy' and his interest in the Association.

As more and more of us are learning about the effect on people of all walks of life, particularly the elderly, of neurological conditions, PSP, one of the grimmer of these, has been shown to be far more common than hitherto understood. It is, I believe, a very individual disease, with which, as it progresses, sufferers, their carers and their families often struggle with too little support. Our Association seeks to redress this, as well as to promote and sponsor research into its cause, effective treatment and eventual cure.

I look forward as your new President to meeting many of you at future PSP events. I hope you will forgive my enforced absence from these at the moment, as I juggle with a large number of conflicting commitments.

With best wishes,

Charles Guthrie"

We had instigated, early on, fortnightly coordinating Meetings, held at Wappenham every other Tuesday, to which all those involved with the charity (other than our Medical Advisory Panel and Trustees), were invited to attend and take part. With a set agenda, the Meeting enabled us to coordinate between different objectives; but, perhaps more importantly, kept everyone aware of what went on, particularly at the heart of the charity's work.

In the early days, Maggie Rose, as our Nurse Specialist, plus Peter Cover, who looked after our Support Groups, would brief us on their work and some of the agonising problems confronting afflicted families across Europe, struggling with this devastating disease as it progressed. As we grew, the Meetings grew larger and more important in keeping all informed. However, to fit everyone in, we had to move the venue from the outbuilding to my house and fortunately large dining room (and the same polished oak table at which this story began).

Although neither Trustees nor our Medical Advisory Panel nor research representatives from London could cost effectively attend, I would, at such meetings, until we could afford a Research Director to take this on, outline research plans discussed with Andrew Lees and our Medical Advisory Panel and their proposals. These Meetings also had a 'brain storming' element, where ideas for and coordination of fundraising events we might plan and run or take part in were discussed and approved. I would also seek to keep Trustees closely up to speed with what was going on.

After the sad death of Brian Fisher, Elizabeth Kennedy, who lived locally, became a Trustee for the next three years before departing to Australia and in 1998, Andrew Fenwick, Nigel Down, Richard Kirby, Peter Glithero, Simon Koe and James Koe also signed up, bringing the total number of Trustees up to eleven.

Andrew Fenwick was a close friend of my eldest son Simon and Financial Director of Brunswick PR. He generously arranged for The PSP Association to be able to use one of their smart Boardrooms off Lincoln's Inn Fields in Central London as well as offering a delicious sandwich working lunch for all our subsequent Trustees' Meetings there.

Nigel Down was a close friend of my son Jamie, working at SEI Investments, also in Central London. Richard is Gerald Kirby's brother and works in Barings. Together with Peter Glithero and my two elder sons, they strengthened impressively our Executive Committee, bringing in considerable financial and City experience, together with much needed 'younger blood'.

In the early days, the outbuildings of my house had proved an ideal location (fortuitously but not surprisingly geographically near the centre of a rough circle of the respective home locations of our growing team) for coordinating the balance of effort across our various objectives. For, at that time in our growth, centralised management was essential to ensure that priorities both between and within our objectives were affordable; and to keep down costs to match income. Hours of work, travel, visits, meetings, information provision and research all had to be carefully rationed to match available funds. In the years ahead, delegation and the setting up of separate directorates would become an increasing priority.

Meanwhile, as the Charity grew, space in the outbuildings at the Old Rectory was becoming more at a premium. Near the end of our time there, we had squeezed in five desks (each one smaller that the last!), all with monitors working to a dual role server, plus our interconnected and impressive Cannon colour copier and scanner. In addition, we networked in three outstations to enable some of our consultants to work from home. Whilst the charity remained at Wappenham, we were effectively limited to four in-house employees, as the outbuildings could not be adapted to meet the laid down requirements for offices with five or more employees.

However, by taking space from the adjacent garage, we were able to cope for several years with the ever increasing files and paperwork accumulating. The garage itself housed our display boards and other sizeable items, such as bulk ordered Christmas Cards and drinks for fund raising events. Pressure to move again to larger purpose built offices continued to mount. In the last two years that we were based at Wappenham, in order to access our stationery, it was necessary to enter the loo and go through a door into a large cupboard! (The space was taken out from the family garage – fortunately still remaining big enough to house a car or trailer).

This was not exactly an ideal solution, even though the extra room behind the loo made a secure home for the more valuable stationary items! We also converted a small additional room on the ground floor of the outbuildings into a growing archive store over this period.

By early 2005, it had become clear that we needed to move as soon as we could find suitable larger but affordable offices, with enough space, which, at that stage of our growth, we planned to rent, not buy. The new Office needed to be within a radius of some ten miles from Towcester, if we were to keep the majority of our team. (Wappenham lies some 4 miles east south east of Towcester).

We needed, to allow for further growth, some 2,500 sq ft (The Old Rectory outbuilding only offered some 1,300). We found several possibilities, from well designed and equipped but expensive-to-rent purpose built offices, within a nearby business park, to a converted barn not far from Wappenham and an unconverted one half way to Daventry to the North.

Having rejected all of these for good reasons, we next looked at some land and barns owned by an Oxford College, for sale, some five miles Northeast of Towcester, for which we put in a bid. For by that time, thanks to a totally unexpected legacy, totalling some £500,000 we could afford to purchase rather than rent; and there were not only some attractive benefits of owning rather that renting, but potential profit for the charity in the site. However, we were, in hindsight, fortunate to have been outbid there, at the last moment, by a property developer. For, the site, unlike the one we eventually bought, was very much 'in the sticks', that is, out of town, and with no post office or even shops nearby.

Then in early 2006, we heard (through Tricia Holmes's intelligence network) that a property in the middle of Towcester, on the main high street of this historic town, was coming on the market. It was a Grade 2 listed building on three floors, which a property developer had bought and was 'doing up' to let as three offices. It had some 3,500 sq ft of office space and, more importantly, had a sizeable car park at the back, almost opposite the new Waitrose supermarket.

Its front door opened onto Watling Street, some two hundred yards from banks, shops and the main Post Office and just across the street from the Town Hall. The 'down side' was that it was, at that time, run down, in major need of restoration, unfurnished, with no carpets or curtains and in need of double glazing at the front and a car park barrier at the back. In addition there was a lot of external and internal renovation work required to make it habitable as charity offices. These were challenging hurdles to be surmounted.

Thanks to our legacy and an unexpected windfall from the TV programme 'Who Wants to be a Millionaire', won for our charity by Lord Coe (as described in the later chapter on 'Fundraising'), we felt, hower, that this was an opportunity we could not afford to pass by. The charity, desperate for more space, could now afford to put in a competitive offer to buy the whole building and to have the renovation work completed to meet its requirements. We drew up a plan accordingly. Our Trustees then debated this plan and after a visit by our Chairman, who recognised its value and was very supportive, I met the developer, John Hutchings, a well known and respected local builder. Some tough and protracted negotiations, involving our Solicitors, Layton's of Carmelite, in London followed; and with the enormously helpful support of Christopher Hobson's local Architectural Partnership, we surveyed the site and negotiated a fair deal. John Hutchings accordingly adjusted his building plan to suit us; to be supervised by our architects. Our solicitors accordingly went ahead on a negotiated exchange of contracts, which took place in the autumn of 2006; with completion on 2nd January 2007.

There was still much work to be done and supervised, including the refurbishing of the building, as well as its carpeting, furnishing, double glazing, heating, air conditioning and lighting. We also needed an IT control system, furniture, room allocation and much other infrastructure, including security and car park arrangements and barrier control.

To help in the coordination of all this and in organising our move in early June (originally planned for May, but delayed due to the late arrival of our new chairs and desks), we were fortunate to find help over our new premises, again through Tricia Holmes, who knew everyone who was anyone in the Towcester area!

Cliff Davies, who had built up a reputation as a Premises Advisor in the area, agreed terms to help and advise us over the move planning and took on the important but tough job of being our part time 'Premises Manager'. He had great experience, knowledge and professionalism in this field and knew all the best building related companies in the area. He played a key role in both our move and our office renovation programme, as did Christopher Hobson, as our architectural advisor.

After a series of planning meetings, we fixed a weekend in June 2007 for our move, which, to save costs, we took on 'in-house', with my PA, Debbie and her husband Rudi hiring a large van into which we loaded a huge number of heavy cardboard boxes full of files and books, all labelled and numbered, by room and directorate.

We had a working party of several staff members at each end (both at Wappenham and at Towcester) on our 'D Day', a Friday. Between us, we loaded all our cardboard boxes and other accessories into the van at one end and lugged them, at the other, either to their allocated room or to the archive room, unfortunately up two long and steep staircases to the top floor of the new offices.

Meanwhile our third team handled the computer equipment and monitors. The toughest load we left to Canon staff. Our massive copier and scanner had to be disassembled, lifted down the stairs at Wappenham (no easy feat!), loaded up, transported to Towcester and manhandled up to the first floor of our new offices. After two earlier aborted attempts (the first with only two then a second try with still only three lifters), a team of four strong men arrived from Canon the following Tuesday and successfully completed the job. It would take over a month to 'bed everything down', but we achieved our aim to be just about up and running on the following Monday morning and sufficiently organised to be able to respond to calls from our subscribers.

Next time, we all agreed to go for a removals firm, though the charity benefited not insubstantially in financial terms from our efforts! However, Health and Safety may not have approved and had there been even a couple more cardboard boxes full of books, the handover of Chief Executives might have taken place considerably earlier, as both our Financial Controller and I could feel our hearts thumping wildly by the twentieth ascent of the stairs!

Shortly after the this heroic move, we invited a local Towcester recruiting company, called, improbably, PSP (Park Street Personnel), to assist us recruit a part time 'Support Administrator' to help with the growing workload of our Care and Support team and website Discussion Forum; and also to assist Gerald Kirby in Office Management, liaising closely with Cliff Davies. We interviewed the candidates they provided and selected Lorraine Bowers, to work part time with Gerald Kirby and part time with our Care and Support Team. Thanks to Lorraine's versatility and close coordination between her, Gerald, Cliff and our Support Directorate, this all worked extremely well.

With the completion of the car park barrier and a security camera on the first floor, our new offices began to look sufficiently professional for us to start to prepare for our Patron's visit and official opening of the New Offices in November 2007, but first there was still much to do.

At this stage, our further recruitment, basic organisation and division of responsibilities were increasingly being shaped by our objectives; which were, to remind readers:

~ the provision of information and support to afflicted families,

~ promoting and sponsoring research worldwide into the cause, effective treatment and eventual cure of PSP across Europe,

~ engendering awareness of PSP and our charity, particularly amongst relevant health and welfare professionals mainly across the UK,

~ and fundraising to bring in the income necessary to take these and other objectives forward.

There was, too, another fast growing responsibility; the professional financial management of income and outgoings to finance the above and the concomitant increasing administrative burden. In order to discuss the issues thrown up by these growing pressures; and how we tackled them, each of the above objectives is addressed in the following four chapters.

This chapter concludes with a brief overview of the ever changing relationship and balance between listed objectives. Subsumed but not stated in the Charity's Mission statement is the relief of suffering of afflicted families, which, until effective treatment and cure is available, must have equal priority – though not necessarily equal funding – to research. Careful assessment of balance between resources spent on research and those spent on care and support is therefore necessary on a regular basis. This balance is likely to be affected by factors such as:

~ research already committed,

~ new research in the pipeline,

~ how external Peer Review rates that new research,

~ The PSP Association's Medical Advisory Panel's recommendations,

~ the proportion of the Charity's available funds needed to meet the above,

~ an assessment of what information and support projects need funding,

~ overall funds available; and the amount the Charity can afford to spend altogether in the period.

Hence fundraising, as always, is the key. The balance between sponsoring research into cause, treatment and cure of PSP, (without which there would be no real hope for the future for patients and their families) and the provision of much needed information and support (desperately needed by those diagnosed as having this disease and their families) is not easy to strike. It often requires, to resolve these conflicting pressures, courage and optimism by Trustees in budgeting income, particularly since expenditure on raising awareness amongst the general pubic as well as amongst relevant health and welfare professionals remains a crucial priority. For; without such raised awareness, the funds we so urgently need would not be forthcoming!

So the broad division of expenditure of income will always pose sensitive and tough questions; the best answer to which is often to make a commitment to increase budgeted income – in effect, getting the fundraising team to work that bit harder!

Although our objectives are each treated separately by chapter, they are nothing like as clear cut as this approach may make them seem. For example, the provision of information is a necessary part of engendering awareness, but is also a key aspect of care and support. Our website and web Discussion Forum serve both purposes and therefore cut across these neat boundaries. Again, the publishing of research engenders awareness amongst the relevant health and welfare professionals; and the cost and effect of adequate care and support on patients' and their carers' quality of life (and, indeed, the prevalence of the disease itself – essential to know to plan required care and support) can only be measured by research.

To help in this balancing act, we set up two Sub Committees:

~ our Financial Sub Committee, which met every other month and consisted of Peter Glithero, our Treasurer, Gerald Kirby, as Financial Controller and the Chief Executive, as Chairman. We looked at current and projected income and outgoings, reserves, investments and balances. We measured progress and methodology against Charity Commissioners' and Company House guidelines and directives. We drafted Business Plans and Reports and Accounts and sought to keep a firm grip on the charity's money. Minutes were kept of important decisions and distributed to Trustees.

~ our Trustees Sub Committee, which met twice a year; in the early Spring to approve a draft Budget and in the early Autumn to approve a draft Report and Accounts. It consisted initially of Our Hon Secretary, Joanna Tomkinson, our Treasurer, Peter Glithero (who both lived up in the Northamptonshire area) and again with the Chief Executive, as Chairman. Joanna

1. *Sara - London '58*

2. *With Lucy-Penang '64*

3. *Cyprus '85*

5. *With Wilson '91*

4. *Courcheval '90*

6. *At Wappenham '94*

1. *The Great Hall, Gayton*

2. *Gayton Manor from the Church*

1. *The Old Rectory, Wappenham*

2. *From the Garden*

3. *Outbuildings on the Left*

1. *The 'Koe Boys' before the Marathon*

2. *Being coached by 'Seb'*

3. *After the coaching*

1. *The kitchen table at Wappenham '94*

2. *Maggie and Tess with Michael at Stowe*

3. *After Caroline's Farewell party - with the team*

1. *Outbuilding: Gerald Kirby at work*

2. *Staff and Trustees' 'Away Day' Oxford 02*

1. *PSP House Towcester from the front*

2. *The Car Park*

3. *From the rear*

1. *Dudley Moore suffering from PSP*

2. *With CBE award at Buckingham Palace*

3. *Nigel Dempster at the PSP Association Concert*

1. *HRH with Ian Barclay at our Symposium*

2. *Maggie Rose, PSP Nurse Specialist*

3. *Volunteer Care Coordinators Lunch '02*

1. *Lord Bramall at the Grosvenor House Reception*

2. *Christopher Miers - Soldier and Artist*

3. *Viewing his Paintings*

4. *HRH chats with Maggie at The PSP Association Grosvenor House Reception*

1. *The PSP Symposium*

2. *The Benadie family at Silverstone fundraising*

3. *Our Staff's Children appeal for funds for The PSP Association's work*

1. *Winning Team Silverstone '00*

2. *Development Officers at Wappenham*

1. *Lord Coe visits Wappenham*

2. *MFAC's First Meeting '04*

3. *MFAC's Fundraising Dinner at the House of Lords*

1. *PSP Association Reception Lord Chancellor's Office*

2. *Guests Spellbound by Seb!*

1. *Skiddaw '99*

2. *Anna Paola, Pianist*

3. *George Melly, Eleanor Bron and Ron Rubin at the concert in memory of Dudley Moore '04*

1. *Daphne Tusa with daughter Helen Barkshire and granddaughter Anna*

2. *Dog Sledding in Sweden*

passed the role of Hon Secretary to Gerald Kirby in 1999, but remained as a Trustee and a member of this sub committee until 2006, when she handed over, having served as a long standing, impressive and loyal Trustee, to Lady Turner (Deborah). Deborah is another good friend with a razor sharp legal mind, who lives in nearby Maidford (in South Northampton-shire) and 'volunteered' (a generous response to my rather desperate plea) to take over as the third member of our sub committee. The putting together of our Report and Accounts became, as the charity grew and as the Government and Charity Commissioners tightened their requirements under SORP for greater transparency and more information, a major annual task.

Report and Accounts, budgeting and other related issues are discussed further in Chapter 8, which gives some details on our administration and finance, but first the following three chapters address each of our major objectives (Information and Support, Research and Awareness) and how we progressed toward them.

4. *Information and support*

T he PSP Association is the only charity in the UK dedicated to 'fighting' PSP. It does so, of course, particularly in the provision of information and support for those with PSP, within a complex framework of prescribed legislation. For the State has a Statutory duty to provide information and support to all patients within the NHS across the whole UK.

Sadly, many are adversely affected as a result of the "unlevel playing field" within the field of care in the UK. For example, in England and Wales nursing care is required to be provided at no cost to the patient, by the State, whilst personal care remains, subject to means testing, the responsibility of the individual; whereas in Scotland both are, within availability and other limitations, provided at no cost to the patient.

Similarly, information about diseases is provided by NHS Direct, but this is not a comprehensive facility. Consequently we, like others in the voluntary sector, seek to improve upon the information, care and support the NHS offers today. Unfortunately, further improvements are still badly needed, particularly in our field i.e. that of neurology, where neurologists, specialist nurses, therapists and other key support remains in desperately short supply.

In the early stage of the Association's growth, one of our key priorities was to augment the scant information about PSP available for those families afflicted by this disease, with a main focus on the UK. We could not, however, just ignore the rest of Europe or even elsewhere, in response to the many desperate emails, telephone calls and letters we received from around the world. For there was not only very little information to be found about PSP within the UK, other than a broad description of 'parkinsonism' under Parkinson's Disease, but little across the rest of Europe and almost none elsewhere outside the USA, Canada and Japan.

To do so effectively, we needed to work out how to reach as many as possible of those families with members suffering from PSP; and to encourage them to join our Association. Although free for those on income support or for those who wished to claim poverty, we settled on £15 a year across Europe and double that elsewhere as a reasonable subscription to help cover some of our costs, including the printing and posting of our information packs.

For those who joined, we sent, by return, information about where to find help and support; and about the disease itself and what could be offered in the way of symptomatic treatment. We would also inform and update subscribers about ongoing and planned research around the world into the cause, treatment and eventual cure of this devastating disease.

In practice, we took on two related but separate main roles:

~ the provision of tailored information, through our telephone counselling service and nurses and through our literature, website etc directly to afflicted families who joined our Association, across Europe;

~   information (tactfully provided) to health and welfare professionals across the UK involved
     in the care and support of PSP patients.

We opted, in 1995, to put out a regular newsletter to all our subscribers and to selected health
and welfare professionals across the world, including all consultant neurologists within the Association of British Neurologists. This newsletter, or Bulletin as we then named it, went out three times
a year, in January, May and September to what has built up to some 2,000 addresses.

Each edition is now also published on our website. It has recently been renamed 'PSP Matters'
and includes, in its new format, with photographs, an editorial and sections on research, support,
awareness and fundraising, along with letters from readers, hints and tips, poems, contact details
etc. The research input is provided by our Research Fellows updating readers on their ongoing PSP
research projects. There is now to be, as a new development, an annual PSP Research Bulletin circulated to relevant readers, mainly in the research field.

With editorial support from our international and impressive Medical Advisory Panel, we set out
also to provide a handbook on PSP – basic information about the disease and its progression, including what treatments are available, and where to look to find help medically, financially and within
the community, through signposting related information sources and support.

We distributed in 1995 our first information booklet, adapted and anglicised, with Professor
Lawrence Golbe's kind permission, from his 'Layman's Guide to PSP', written for the US Society
for PSP two years earlier.

Our Guide was then edited by Professor Andrew Lees and distributed widely across the UK
(and to those who subscribed to our Association in other European Countries). The Association of
British Neurologists agreed to send copies to all consultant neurologists 'on their books' and it was
also circulated to Primary Care Trusts, to ophthalmologists, to geriatricians, to nurse specialists,
speech and language therapists and to centres of neurological excellence across the UK, as well as
to patients and their carers on joining our Association.

Several years later, we produced, under the direction of our then new Director of Care and Support, John Chandler, a comprehensive and authoritative Carer's Information Pack (CIP) to super-
sede our earlier and simpler version. This later CIP, now regularly updated, covers a wide range of
related subjects, including about PSP, living with the disease, work, benefits and finance and getting
about. It also includes chapters on movement and mobility, speech and communications, swallowing, eating and drinking, behavioural changes, bowel and bladder, and 'Into Hospital' (information
for Ward Staff).

We also now offer, upon request (usually later in the progress of the disease), chapters on legal
issues, nursing and continuing care. There are also sections on Percutaneous Endoscopic Gastrostomy (PEG), or tube, feeding, as eating, drinking and swallowing become too difficult and dangerous
for the patient, and on brain donation after death from both from patients and carers. Such generous
donations remain absolutely vital for essential pathological research.

We also set about establishing a comprehensive website to raise awareness and provide information about PSP and about our charity worldwide. The first edition of this was finally up and running, after some hiccups, in early 1999, leading to queries about PSP from around the World. Those across Europe, we handled. Those from the USA and Canada, we passed to our sister charity in the USA, now named CurePSP. Elsewhere, we do our best to answer queries and share out the workload with CurePSP. In particular, we have developed a strong link with the Parkinson's Disease Association in Victoria, Australia, with its embryonic PSP group there.

With the proliferation of information on the web, there is a growing problem for those seeking to sort out information that is accurate from that which is not – 'the wheat from the chaff'. 'Kite Marking' has been suggested and is shortly to be trialled in the UK, but this raises issues about who judges authenticity. We accordingly research carefully the information we provide and advise our readers to be careful in checking advice from sites they do not know.

Over time, the value of our website and our own recognition of its importance to those families afflicted by PSP had grown sharply; and we accordingly devote an increasing amount of time and effort in updating and improving its content. We opened, in 2003, a Discussion Forum on the site. The website was completely redesigned in 2005 and a further major overhaul and update is underway to bring it to the forefront of fast moving technology in this field.

Our Discussion Forum also grew fast, under the auspices of our Care and Support Directorate, requiring, we found, ever more resources to monitor and provide appropriate responses, where required. Early on, we had to learn a sharp lesson on the need for a simple password system to defeat machine generated spam and porn which threatened to flood and destroy our Forum. Thereafter, the bulk of the postings we received were from Carers with queries or stories. These were mainly emailed from the UK and the rest of Europe. However, we also receive and respond to queries through the Discussion Forum worldwide including, for example, from Japan, India, Israel and Cyprus; and use it to seek to help establish similar PSP focussed organisations elsewhere in the world.

Maggie Rose's role as our first Nurse Specialist, was outlined in Chapter 2. In July 1997, she moved with her family up to Shropshire, but fortunately for us and for PSP afflicted families, agreed to continue operating an answer phone and counselling service from there. We were very aware by then of what a vital aspect of the Association's work this was.

Maggie had been working from home in Gayton, taking some twenty calls a week, mainly in the evening. The number of these calls was steadily increasing. Some were routine and straightforward, but many were desperate cries for help, sometimes late into the night and some extremely stressful and demanding. Maggie would brief me with graphic details of these calls immediately before our fortnightly meetings – and, at the Meetings, whilst retaining confidentiality, give a painfully clear picture to those attending, of their nature

Her debriefing included details of the sometimes appalling treatment patients and their carers reported receiving from, we suspected, overworked staff at Nursing and Care Homes and, regrettably, too, about shameful and disgraceful treatment from nurses within the NHS. To be fair, we usually only heard one side of the story; and we also learnt about many wonderful nurses, working in hospitals, in nursing homes or visiting patients at home, going to astonishing lengths to provide much needed help and support. We learnt too of the importance and value of palliative care for those in the late stages of this brutal disease and about 'black holes', that is areas and postcodes, where support was seriously inadequate, usually through lack of staff, over-stretched resources or lack of understanding of PSP itself.

Peter Cover had met Grace Lewis at a social event in March 1997. She was a qualified nurse, married with two small children, attractive and likeable and a good listener, with great Irish charm; and unemployed at the time, although just about to start a part time job in a kindergarten! In light of the rapidly increasing number of incoming calls to Maggie, we invited Grace to join our team and were more than delighted when she accepted.

The arrangement we made was that Maggie would continue to take calls from, and look after those who lived North of Northampton and continue to 'keep' those South of Northampton who had already 'got to know her', whilst Grace would take on the rest; though both would back each other up and take calls when the other was not contactable for any reason, particularly in the evenings and at weekends; and in any emergency.

Over the next two years, Maggie and Grace handled an astonishing number of such calls and also attended, with Peter Cover, our Support Group Meetings around the country. The many warm and grateful 'thank you' letters we received from afflicted families, extolling the crucial support provided by our Telephone Counselling Service, made moving reading and heartened our nurses, who put in many unsocial hours in handling often stressful and desperate calls for help.

By the end of 1999, with two young and increasingly demanding children, and a home to run as well as her growing work in her kindergarten, Grace sadly recognised that she had to cut down on her work load. She felt she could, in the future only manage one morning a week with us, and would reluctantly have to give up her evening telephone counselling service. However, she continued to cheer us up with her Monday morning visits to our HQ, which we asked her to use to re-contact those who had joined our Association over six months previously, but with whom we had 'lost touch'. This proved to be a very useful service, but we urgently needed another Telephone Counselling Nurse.

Fortunately for us, Tess Astbury, who worked part time in the neurology department of Northampton General Hospital as a qualified nurse, had heard of us through Dr Paul Davies, her Neurologist, whom we knew well. He had been in post when Sara had been admitted to Northampton General Hospital.

Tess generously agreed to take over the Telephone Counselling Service in the South from Grace, anyway until we could find a more permanent replacement. Tess was very caring, warm and fun, with excellent working knowledge of neurodegenerative diseases. For the next two years, she and Maggie then took on the steadily increasing telephone counselling load and other nurse specialist work we had by then adopted.

Meanwhile, the Parkinson's Disease Society had successfully 'pump primed' Parkinson Disease Nurse Specialists (PDNS) into the NHS, with the Department of Health accepting and eventually funding the bulk of the costs of these posts. The Multiple Sclerosis (MS) Society followed suit and soon the NHS were funding MS Nurse Specialists too. We sought to 'get on' the same 'bandwagon' as these larger charities and accordingly approached the National Hospital for Neurology to seek to negotiate a similar deal, though on a much smaller scale. Our aim was to pump prime one Nurse Specialist within the NHS. This, we learnt the hard way, would take much time and patience.

We either didn't have the clout or perhaps just the timing, finesse and charm of the larger charities. Clearly the NHS was not, at this stage, going to pay for Nurse Specialists for each and every neurodegenerative disease, particularly as the days of financial plenty had gone and PCTs were under huge pressure to make savings. Nonetheless, there remains today a compelling argument for the NHS to employ a range of Nurse Specialists to look after **all those** with rapidly progressive neurodegenerative diseases, along the lines of a very successful recent trial in West Berkshire. That would mean not just specialist nurses supporting the better known such diseases (having been pump primed by the larger charities) within the NHS.

The plan we eventually agreed with the National Hospital for Neurology was for The PSP Association to pay in full for the first year's work of a PSP Nurse Specialist, with the selected candidate working half her time with the National Hospital and half with us as a telephone counselling nurse. Thereafter, it was agreed that the NHS would pay at least half her costs.

After a lengthy NHS recruitment process (which for a series of what we regarded as bureaucratic, heavy handed, top down managerial processes and what doubtless they regarded as necessary procedures) took over a year, Cathy Magee, a Parkinson's Disease Nurse Specialist, was appointed as a PSP Nurse specialist giving us half her time and the hospital the other half, but not before Maggie had single-handedly carried our evening telephone counselling over that period, as Tess had had to return to her mainstream work.

To make matters worse, unfortunately, a few months later, Cathy was offered another better paid job she could not refuse and we were back to the drawing board, having paid in full for that period of her shared work for us and the Hospital. We decided that particular route at that particular time, with the NHS cutting back sharply, was not cost effective, so, temporarily anyway, abandoned our pump priming scheme; and advertised for candidates along the lines Maggie worked – that is, for us alone!

By this time, we really needed not just one but two additional Nurse Specialists, one for the South West of England and one for the South East. By early 2007, we had found the two we needed; Jill Lyons in Somerset and Samantha Pavey in Surrey, both of whom quickly settled into their new roles. Both were friendly, capable fully trained nurses with suitable backgrounds and both have proved to be excellent choices and popular with our subscribers.

By then, we had formally given our Nurse Specialists additional roles to add to their telephone counselling and their attendance at Local Support Group Meetings within their area. The first was to spearhead our campaign to raise the profile of PSP amongst relevant health and welfare professionals, offering them as described later in Chapter 6, opportunities to attend awareness talks across the country. The second was to attend specialist clinics at as many Centres of Neurological excellence as possible. Neurologists at such clinics warmly welcomed them. These visits enabled our nurses to meet early on many of the patients, whose families would later join our Association. (In fact, Maggie, for some while, had already blazed the trail by undertaking these additional roles on an opportunity basis).

With the size of our charity, it was not practical, even at the later stages of our growth, for us to attempt to visit individually all those patients and carers joining our Association. Yet we recognised the need for those trying to look after someone with this disease to talk to others 'in the same boat' and be briefed on ongoing research and various support initiatives by our team on a reasonably regular basis.

So, accordingly, as mentioned earlier, we set up Local Support Groups across the country. Each such Group met at a designated geographic location. All carers (and others we felt might be interested), who lived within a reasonable distance from that location, would receive from Peter Cover, our Local Support Group Coordinator, an invitation to attend a specific meeting on a specific day.

The location of these meetings was selected primarily to suit carers in the area, taking account of factors such as where PSP afflicted families in that area lived and assessed travel time to a suitable group location. This was, to an extent, dictated by availability, affordability and opportunity; and by Peter Cover's map analysis of time and distance, which, taken together, limited the geographic spread of each group's catchment area. We began with some twelve such groups across the UK, but these grew to sixteen by 2007, (including one in Northern Ireland and two in Scotland) and recently to over twenty. Meeting locations vary from a PSP afflicted family's home, or a room in a hospital, to a village hall and even a church.

Peter Cover and the Nurse Specialist, within whose area the Group was located, travelled to such meetings by car, train or air or sometimes by a combination of such travel modes. On flights, Maggie would regularly find herself waiting anxiously at check in for a cheerful unflustered Peter to breeze up 30 seconds before flight closure. At the Meeting, they met those who came to listen or join in the debate. Peter and our nurse would then steer and regulate the meeting, answer concerns, update the Group on progress, particularly in care and research and ensure everyone had a chance to ask questions and actively participate.

Our team sought to visit each Local Support Group at least three times a year. 'All in the same boat' was an accurate rallying cry for these Groups, though, in a rapidly progressing disease, it was not always easy to handle the wide differences in problems faced by those recently diagnosed and those in the end stages of the disease, with both groups often present at the meeting. For that reason alone, we gently discouraged attendance by patients. For, a carer of someone just diagnosed and starting their journey with PSP could be deeply shocked by the presence of a patient in the later stages of the disease, wheelchair bound, with fixed gaze and perhaps unable to speak; and discussion of some of the problems faced by families in the final stages of the disease would tend to be inhibited by their presence.

Sometimes, a carer with a strong personality would dominate a group and considerable judgement and understanding was needed to facilitate such meetings. As to numbers attending, it could be difficult for a carer caring for someone with PSP to come at all, particularly as the disease progressed. Their role was often stressful and exhausting and it was not always possible to find someone to take on their 'duties' at home and care for 'their' patient whom they would have to leave behind. Distance and travel time could also be a further disincentive.

We established a simple SAE form for carers to respond to an invite, but decisions about coming were usually last minute. So Groups tended to vary in size unpredictably, from a disappointing two or three to a packed thirty to forty.

On one occasion, Peter and Maggie drove up to Barnsley to be met by the entire family of one patient and no-one else. The lovely thank you letter sent by the wife of the family member with PSP made us realise just how important such visits were; even one like that for just one family. However, such meetings were not cheap, taking account of travel and other expenses, and a balance had to be struck in cost effectiveness against the other support that amount of money could provide.

We sought help from carers and friends of carers who were prepared to become 'Volunteer Local Support Group Coordinators'. Some offered their homes as meeting venues, some organised coffee and sandwiches and some helped Peter in organising and running the meetings themselves. We held an annual 'thank you' coordinator's lunch at the Old Rectory at Wappenham.

Peter Cover and his wife, Kim, had a house in France, which they lived in over the summer. Whether it was the English summers, the French vineyards, just time for a change now that their children were grown up, or even his speeding points (collected whilst hurrying north to a Support Group Meeting), they decided to live in France pretty well permanently; which sadly meant Peter handing over his work as Local Support Group Coordinator.

We advertised, amongst other places, through the Officers Association. Air Commodore John Chandler CBE, who had recently left the Royal Air Force and was working part time for the Parole Board, applied to take on what had become a wider role as Director of Care and Support, on the understanding that we would within a year, bring in a Deputy as an employee. This move enabled us to place our Nurse Specialists and newly recruited Regional Development Officers under his wing, as well as our Support Groups and Support Back Up team.

John Chandler, working largely from home, soon had our whole care and support operation running smoothly and efficiently and, at the same time, took on the supervision and overall editorship of our new Carers Information Pack, described earlier.

The overriding need to engender greater awareness within the relevant health and welfare professionals across the country led us to fundraise for, and recruit, additional Regional Development Officers. This initiative is described in more detail under Chapter Six, but the major role of these appointments was in extending the care and support we were able to provide; so responsibility for their oversight and management was given to John, as our then Director of Care and Support. Their job description included three roles; to network with health and welfare professionals in their area, to monitor progress of the implementation of the National Service Framework for Long Term Neurological Conditions and to provide a link between carers and people with PSP and relevant NHS professionals, attending support group meetings in their areas.

We held our first Symposium at the National Hospital for Neurology and Neurosurgery in October 1995, attended by carers and therapists – some 90 people in all. To allow uninhibited briefings about the progress of the disease, we discouraged patients attending too (though our policy was to let them come, if the patient was keen to be there and prepared to hear possibly upsetting details about the progress of the disease). Some carers travelled great distances to attend. In the morning the speakers, all leading neurologists, focussed on what was PSP, its history, its possible causes, research into its mechanisms, strategies for possible treatment and eventual cure and related subjects. We then held a buffet lunch allowing sufficient time to enable groups to 'network' and question speakers informally – and, to enable us to catch up and 'get back on schedule' if we had overrun in the morning!

In the afternoon, therapists, nurses and social services spoke about care and support for people with PSP and their carers. We were fortunate to have a very impressive group of speakers and an enthusiastic audience, from whom we learnt much at a lively Open Forum we held at the end. We invited a senior neurologist (usually selected by Professor Lees) to chair each Symposium.

The obvious need for and success of our first Symposium, led us to initiate annual Symposia. By the end of 2007, we had held thirteen, with venues including Liverpool, Newcastle, Sheffield, Cambridge, Oxford, Bristol and London, for we sought different teaching hospitals or other suitable venues around the country, aiming to select and rotate locations to ensure that, over time, everyone had a venue in their part of the country. Our Patron, HRH The Duchess of Gloucester, GCVO generously gave time to come to three of these to meet and mingle with carers over coffee; on the last occasion at the Royal College of Obstetricians and Gynaecologists. A growing number of doctors, nurses and therapists also attended our Symposia and thereby added value.

After our move to our new Offices in Towcester, we were able to take on more staff, to handle the additional services we wanted to be able to offer the increasing number of carers and people with PSP joining the Association. We advertised for and interviewed several candidates for the post of Deputy Director of Care and Support. Again, we were fortunate; and in June 2007 we took on

Debra Chand, as John Chandler's deputy. She had been known by and strongly recommended by Nigel Slater, was by then helping us as a consultant to develop our fundraising capacity. He had worked with her for three years at the Leprosy Mission, since leaving which she had been living in Kent and acquiring an MBA. She had also been a local volunteer with Age Concern. Her family were moving up to the Peterborough area to be closer to her parents. We soon learnt what an excellent choice we had made!

Until effective treatment and a cure is found for PSP, the level of care and support required as the disease inexorably advances, increases rapidly, with greater emphasis on the need for palliative care and 'care for the carer'. The full implementation of the Quality Requirements of the National Service Framework for Long Term Neurological Conditions will go a long way toward the National Heath Service being able to provide this, but meanwhile, as the Care and Support services offered by our Association increase, they need careful balancing in the allocation of resources with the contribution we can afford toward research (looked at in the next Chapter), within the overall funds we are able to raise.

5. *Research*

This Chapter looks at aspects of thirteen years of research into PSP, in which The PSP Association has been directly or indirectly involved. It starts with the perceived needs in the research field into this disease in 1993 and follows broadly the chronological progress made from then. Although the focus of The PSP Association has been on treatment and cure, identifying, diagnosing accurately and defining the disease and its prevalence across the UK have been seen as essential steps on the way.

PSP is an adult person's disease, which appears to strike at random those over 40 years of age, with prevalence increasing with age. As average life expectancy increases, so will the number of people with neurodegenerative diseases like PSP. The pollution of our environment with neuro-toxins is compounding the problem. Numbers of people with such diseases across the world will almost certainly continue rapidly to increase, until treatment and cures are found.

Advice from our Medical Advisory Panel, our biennial International Medical Workshops, close liaison with the work of our sister charity, CurePSP and research into related diseases, such as Alzheimer's and Parkinson's were, we saw, the keys to us being able to unleash effective research into treatment and, ultimately, the cure of PSP. Hence, too, the importance of the research centre we were to help establish in London and the other centres of neurological excellence focussing on this devastating disease across the UK and around the world.

Professor Andrew Lees, Chairman of our Medical Advisory Panel and, since 2005, a Trustee of the Association, has played a key and remarkably effective role over the whole period of the charity's life to date, in the drawing together and development of a logical, coherent and forward looking research strategy, coordinated closely with other international research across the world, toward its goal of effective treatment and cure for PSP.

His Foreword to Professors Irene Litvan and Yves Agid's book, 'Clinical and Research Approaches in Progressive Supranuclear Palsy', describes evocatively a physician's view of a patient with PSP[6]:

"Yet in its fully expressed form it presents one of the most arresting and distressing images in neurology. Like that of the Mona Lisa, the hypnotic immutable stare [of the patient] fixes the physician's attention and draws him or her compellingly to the bedside. David de Jong [an eminent neurologist] likened the gait of these pa-tients to that of a dancing bear or marionette bereft of several vital strings. Unforgettable too is the profound catatonic hyperextended arc de cercle and the painful slow, maladroit willed movement. The voice is a haunt-ing, halting preservative drawl, and catastrophic falls backward are an alarming early complaint. Despite this signal appearance, the condition is frequently unrecognised; it is lumped indiscriminately with a hotchpotch of ill-defined heterogeneous system degenerations, mislabelled as Alzheimer's or Parkinson's disease, or dismissed as due to multiple strokes. It can present in unusual ways without any evidence of dementia, with dementia, or

6. *Progressive Supranuclear Palsy – Clinical and Research Approaches by Irene Litvan and Yves Agid 1992 Oxford University Press*

with akinesia alone."

Like other neurodegenerative diseases, Progressive Supranuclear Palsy involves, as described in more detail earlier, the progressive death of neurons, mainly in the brainstem and basal ganglia, just above the nuclei.

As these neurons die, neurofibrillary tangles comprising Tau, a protein which forms the micro-tubular scaffolding for these neurons, are deposited in the brain. Similar tangles of Tau are deposited in Alzheimer's Disease (though in Alzheimer's this occurs mainly in the forebrain – hence dementia). In Parkinson's Disease, Lewy Bodies rather than Tau, are deposited in similar areas of the brain to PSP. In both PSP and Alzheimer's, the Tau protein becomes abnormally hyperphosphorylated; that is, it develops an excess of phosphate, which may be the cause or maybe the effect of the disease.

Without an effective programme of research, there would be no real hope for the future for those diagnosed as having diseases like PSP, which slowly, but surely, take away those capabilities which make life worth living. The abilities to balance, to move, to see, to speak and to swallow are ones we cheerfully take for granted.

Many of the devastating effects and progressive symptoms of PSP have already been described earlier in Chapters One and Four. One additional and sometimes bewildering aspect of this disease is its effect on the personality of the patient. It is often difficult to distinguish between the natural depression of knowing you have a disease like this and that caused by the disease. The latter can lead to emotional lability (crying and laughing without good reason to do so) and sometimes aggressiveness and related personality disorders. This adds further stress and anxiety to the whole family and/or carer, usually unaware that this change (sometimes no more that an exaggeration of previous behaviour patterns) in personality is the 'fault' of the disease and not that of their 'loved one'.

For most PSP patients, even in the later stages of their disease, their intellect remains largely intact, but communication with the outside world becomes increasingly difficult, as their reading, writing and viewing capabilities deteriorate. In these circumstances, it is not surprising that death can sometimes become something for the sufferer to look forward to or even eagerly await. For all the above reasons, there is an urgent need for effective research worldwide into the cause, effective treatment and cure of PSP, a key priority for our Association. Where to start and what was possible/and affordable were key questions we needed to address with the help of our Medical Advisory Panel, once the Charity was formed.

Early on, we had joined the Association of Medical Research Charities and followed their advice and guidelines and that of our distinguished Medical Advisory Panel in sponsoring and promoting research, in advertising for research fellows and in handling their applications. At the outset, we first sought to find out what research had already been carried out into PSP around the world, what research would be most cost effective to sponsor or promote; how to recruit scientists to carry this out and to take us further down the route to our research objectives. How much research could we afford to take on each year, as we grew? Clearly not a lot at the start!

Research costs, particularly those involving clinical trials, were likely well to exceed the Charity's own available resources. Trustees needed to assess annually the amount of funds the Charity could afford to spend itself in sponsoring research and how much of its resources should go into promotion of research by Government and outside bodies.

Although by 2007, The PSP Association had spent well over two million pounds on research since it was founded in 1994, this level of expenditure is 'small beer' in research terms. Increasingly, its strategy has been to seek to pump prime investment by other better endowed bodies, like the Medical Research Council. We recognised early on that neurodegenerative diseases, including PSP, needed to be moved up the political agenda with decision makers being made more aware of the prevalence and the cost, in financial as well as human terms, of these devastating diseases. Our Vice President Research, Professor Colin Blakemore's appointment as Chief Executive of the Medical Research Council was particularly well received by the neurological sector.

In funding research, there is, of course, a close link between sponsorship and promotion. By careful selection of research to sponsor, the Charity has been able to 'pump prime' more expensive transitional and clinical research. Two examples of this, described late in this Chapter, are the UK's Medical Research Council picking up research undertaken by Drs Huw Morris and Rohan de Silva, initially sponsored by The PSP Association and the prospective US/UK Lithium Trial, which has grown out of research sponsored by The PSP Association in the UK and CurePSP in the USA.

About eighteen months after Sara was diagnosed as having PSP, a Dr Peter Pramstaller, a neurologist from Bolzano in Italy, then on a year's attachment to The Institute of Neurology in London, visited us at Gayton Manor to examine Sara and check how her drug regime was working. We much enjoyed his visit and company and promised to keep in touch. He was to play an important role as our first researcher and in the subsequent development of research into PSP and related disorders across Europe.

Peter Pramstaller, born in 1960, is Italian, but speaks fluent English and German as well as his native tongue. He currently lives in Northern Italy. I have been to his house and met there his attractive wife and first born son, who was two years old at the time of my visit. From January to August 1994, he had worked as a Clinical Research Fellow to Professor C D Marsden, a world renowned neurologist, then to Professor Lees, at the Institute of Neurology in London.

Following the advice of our Medical Advisory Panel, our Trustees agreed to sponsor a Project in which Dr Pramstaller would carry out a six month programme of research for The PSP Association. He was to collect and collate all existing research worldwide into PSP using 'Reference Manager' (a computer software package), thereby helping identify gaps and promising areas for research in this field; and to draw up a familial questionnaire, which we would circulate to PSP afflicted families to complete, to trace back family linkages and look at cause of death, in order to obtain evidence of possible genetic susceptibility. The sample size was some two hundred completed returns, mainly from patients on our database. To the considerable relief of many anxious PSP afflicted families, this research found no proven evidence of any parent with PSP in the UK passing the disease down to their offspring, though there were rare examples of this happening elsewhere in the world and anecdotal accounts of such families in the UK, so the jury still remained 'out' on familial genetic susceptibility in PSP. However, it was clear that, unlike in some neurodegenerative diseases, such as Huntingdon's Disease, the risks are extremely low. Even those susceptible are statistically more likely to be hit by the proverbial bus than 'get' PSP.

At the turn of the century, there were many theories as to the cause of PSP, which some believed to be purely environmental, such as from a virus (possibly related to post encephalitic parkinsonism, or Von Economo's Disease, a condition of viral origin). Others believed that there were both environmental and genetic factors involved, but no-one really knew for sure. The few such studies that had been carried out into PSP involved limited numbers (maximum sample some 100,000 of population); and suggested a prevalence of a little over one per 100,000 of population. Leading neurologists were uneasily aware that these prevalence figures obtained were distinctly low – but how low no-one knew.

After Dr Pramstaller's return to Bolzano, we kept in close touch and invited him to become The PSP Association's 'Medical Coordinator, Europe' and to help us in setting up an Italian PSP website, which he successfully did. He later started up a major project, backed by the Italian Government, called Project GenNova, looking at the epidemiology of Parkinson's Disease, PSP and Multiple System Atrophy in the Tyrol. This area is known as a geographical isolate, since, rather like Iceland, the population has been isolated over time by natural barriers and is well suited to genetic linkage studies.

Dr Pramstaller's initial report and our subsequent first International Medical Workshop, outlined later, pointed to prevalence studies and genetic susceptibility being high priorities. There was a need for a preferably country-wide epidemiological study into PSP to establish its prevalence and provide further evidence about a possible genetic component to the disease.

Before addressing these priorities, three pieces of early 'opportunity' research sponsored by The PSP Association are briefly described below; the first looked into our concern about the behavioural effects of PSP, the second was an example of a mini trial into the effects of nicotine patches, and the third looked at a better way of measuring the quality of life of a PSP patient.

Very soon after our first Trustees Meeting, we accepted the recommendation of our Medical Advisory Panel to offer, in 1996, £12,500 toward the first year, and £3,600 a year for the second two years of a three year research study into the effects of PSP on behaviour. Dr Thomas Bak is a thorough, correct, articulate and very likeable neuro-psychologist, whom we came to know well. He undertook, under the direction of Professor John Hodges, at the Cognitive and Brain Science Unit at Addenbrooke's Hospital, Cambridge, this study into the neuro-psychological, neuro-psychiatric and behavioural effects of PSP and related neurodegenerative diseases on patients; reflecting our concern about these distressing problems.

Dr Bak sought PSP patients living within a rough circle of some sixty mile radius from Cambridge, to take part in his three year longitudinal research project. This sponsorship helped link us in more closely with Addenbrooke's Hospital, a centre of neurological excellence; and enabled this important study and aspect of PSP successfully to be completed. The project actually took almost four years. It concluded that PSP, as well as Alzheimer's and other related disease groups, was significantly impaired in relation to controls in all cognitive tests, though in PSP slowness in response, rather than recall, supported the view that the higher intellect of PSP patients was largely left intact. Levels of impairment in these diseases could, in future, be measured using scales drawn up in this research, now known as the Addenbrooke Cognitive Examination or ACE[7].

Dr Andrew Churchyard came over from Australia in 1996 for a six month attachment to the Institute of Neurology, under the direction of Professor Andrew Lees. They were both well aware that PSP causes deficiencies in the levels of many naturally occurring brain chemicals or transmitters, such as acetylcholine. Based on anecdotal evidence that smoking alleviated related symptoms, Dr Churchyard, before returning to Australia, ran a small user trial, with volunteers, into whether the use of nicotine patches might help people with PSP. This trial was completed and published in 1997[8]. Sadly, the results were negative, but it had been worth a try and gave our subscribers confidence that no research stone was being left unturned into any potential disease modifying treatment. Indirectly, it also led later to further research in Newcastle upon Tyne, sponsored by The PSP Association, into the brain's transmitters and receptors.

Meanwhile, Peter Cover sought, when the subject of nicotine was raised at our Local Support Groups, tactfully to discourage PSP afflicted families who had heard about this as a possible treatment, from going out and buying patches or even taking up smoking! The patient and carer grapevine is very sensitive to research possibilities and the former are extremely keen to volunteer for trials of drugs which might help, however 'long shot' and, often, however risky, as they feel they have nothing to lose.

A careful balance has to be drawn between funds spent on research into treatment and cure and related research; and funds spent on improving the quality of life of living patients and all that this involves. Our progress on the former is described below; the latter, including investment in alternative medicine, has already largely been covered in the previous chapters, but research the Charity has sponsored into quality of life and its measurement needs a brief mention here.

In the Autumn of 2001, Dr Anette Schrag proposed to undertake a three year research project to devise an internationally acceptable 'Instrument for Measuring the Quality of Life' for PSP patients. Hitherto, this had been assessed using either a generic scale or a Parkinson's Disease instrument, neither of which properly addresses nor measures key concerns of PSP patients and carers. Furthermore, because of the high levels of disability associated with PSP, these scales are prone to 'ceiling

7. *Cognitive bedside assessment, T. Bak et al, Journal of Neurology, Neurosurgery and Psychiatry 2004 Topic 36*
8. *Churchyard et al. Effects of nicotine patches in progressive supranuclear palsy 1997*

effects' (that is, the score reaches the upper limit quite quickly and cannot go up any further).

The PSP Association agreed to sponsor the first two years of Dr Schrag's Project and assist her in the distribution of her questionnaire to patients and carers on our database, and to handle and anonymise responses to protect patient confidentiality. The US Society sponsored her third year's work, during which she sent the questionnaire to US patients and carers for their response. This important patient and carer data from the two countries provided the basis of her Instrument, now internationally accepted.

When Jenny Mais' grandfather, Colin Thompson, was diagnosed as having PSP, Jenny learnt about the various aspects and challenges of caring for someone with this disease. In 2003, she took a degree in Social Psychology at Loughborough University and chose this as her subject for her degree dissertation. We helped her in circulating a questionnaire she had put together on quality of life for carers and for patients with PSP and provided her with anonymised responses.

Her dissertation, a bound copy of which she sent us, highlighted many issues and concerns raised by the nearly two hundred responses we received from patients and carers on our database. We used this in our submission to the Department of Health, putting our case for much greater support and back up for PSP patients, as part of the evidence they sought in drafting the then new National Framework for Long Term Neurological Conditions.

Following Dr Pramstaller's interim report, we held our first 'brain storming' International Medical Workshop on 24th and 25th September 1996, at the Marie Curie Institute near Oxted in Surrey, courtesy of Sir Michael Carleton-Smith, then still Chief Executive of Marie Curie Cancer Care. This Meeting, a gathering of some sixty of the world's leading scientists in this field, was, like subsequent Workshops, chaired by Professor Andrew Lees. Its aim was primarily to seek to identify the most cost effective research for The PSP Association to sponsor, taking account of what was already being sponsored by our sister charity, CurePSP, and any other sponsored research into PSP. At that time, there was precious little.

The clear consensus of the workshop was to focus on **genetic** aspects of PSP. (It was some ten years later that Professor Irene Litvan took up a $3 million grant from the US National Institutes for Health to research into possible **environmental** factors. Anecdotally, carers often suggest possible environmental causes or triggers for PSP, such as a blow to the head, leaded petrol, pesticides, the ozone layer, mobile telephones or mercury. Most neurologists agree that all or any of these could trigger the disease in those with genetic susceptibility, but following up these anecdotal linkages with compelling scientific trials is a massive research undertaking, even with a $3 million grant!).

The findings of our first - and very successful, we felt - International Medical Workshop (and all subsequent Workshop abstracts) were published in the prestigious 'Movement Disorders Journal' and led directly to the Charity sponsoring a two year research Project, starting in January 1997, into genetic aspects of PSP.

After the Workshop, a Reception and Dinner for delegates was held that evening at the historic Grade 1 listed Squerries Court, (by kind permission of the Hon. Mrs John Ward); and a private tour of Chartwell the next morning, all generously arranged and organised by Sir John Greenaway and his friends in the area.

The subsequent two year Research Project was undertaken by Dr Huw Morris, a brilliant young scientist, under the direction of Professor Nick Wood, at the Institute of Neurology. The study concluded that there **was** a genetic component to PSP, but a complex one with low risk. Dr Morris's research, and other International research into this, is described later on in this Chapter.

Over the next eleven years following our first Workshop at Oxted, The PSP Association held biennially a total of five further International Medical Workshops; three in the magnificent State Rooms at Stowe School in Buckinghamshire and two at the Institute of Neurology in London, all attended by leading scientists from around the world[9].

Those Workshops we held at Stowe were not only conveniently nearby for the Charity to organise, but provided an unusual, historic and attractive setting. On each occasion, the meeting was followed by a formal dinner for delegates, twice (to impress our US delegates!) at nearby Sulgrave Manor, the ancestral home of George Washington.

These Workshops dovetailed into similar Workshops held in the USA by CurePSP (and with other scientific gatherings looking into aspects of parkinsonism under the Parkinson's Disease umbrella in Europe and around the world).

Our second Workshop focussed on the prevalence of PSP in the UK and the numbers of living patients; and led directly to Dr Uma Nath's epidemiological study, described below.

One of our major early concerns after the Association was registered was the apparent lack of certainty within the scientific community about the number of living PSP patients across the UK and, for us, how to reach them and/or their carers. For whatever reason, it was clear that there was a high level of misdiagnosis and even non-diagnosis of PSP across the UK, particularly amongst older patients away from centres of neurological excellence.

Over our first year following registration, we instigated a simple 'spot check' survey of the location of PSP afflicted families. Whenever a patient or carer joined our Association, we put a pin marking their home location on a map of the UK. Clusters of PSP patients around Centres of Neurological excellence, where knowledge of PSP and its symptoms and the related the standard of diagnosis was high, soon became apparent on our map. In other areas, it remained largely unpunctured and in some quite large swathes of the country were almost totally blank. The South West of England, Northern Ireland, Scotland and the North West of England were, in particular, very 'light' in numbers of diagnosed living PSP patients.

There were several possible reasons for this, the most obvious being that a large number of living patients in those areas had either decided not to join our Association or had never heard of us.

9. *See respective Movement Disorders Journals*

However, it was more than likely - in light of the difficulties in diagnosis of this disease - that at least some PSP patients there were being misdiagnosed or left undiagnosed.

We also noted that just over one in three of those joining our Association had previously been given a different diagnosis, varying from a stroke or brain tumour to one of a range of neurodegenerative diseases, including Alzheimer's disease and Motor Neurone Disease though, most commonly, it was Parkinson's Disease.

A then recent study by Dr Sue Daniel and Professor Lees in 1997 had established the startling fact that more than fifty percent of patients with PSP[10] in the UK were clinically unrecognised and misdiagnosed as having idiopathic Parkinson's Disease.

Related work by Professors Lawrence Golbe and Irene Litvan, taking account the classical eye problems of upgaze and downgaze in PSP, had set out what were to become international criteria, including restricted voluntary eye movement, for clinical diagnosis[11] of PSP, so a diagnosis of 'probable' PSP was only given for those who symptoms fell within this category.

Some of the difficulties facing clinicians over diagnosis were later partially explained by research [12] by Dr David Williams, an Australian Neurologist, who was attached in 2006 to Professor Andrew Lees's Team at the Institute of Neurology for what turned out to be a very productive three year sabbatical, before returning to Australia. During this attachment, he identified a PSP variant, with late onset and/or without eye problems, which behaves very similarly to Parkinson's Disease throughout its course. This variant is now described as PSP-Parkinson's to distinguish it from the classic PSP-Richardson, but even that in its early stages can also closely mimic Parkinson's Disease.

Professor Lees recently acknowledged that a good neurologist was doing well, set against later pathological examination (the 'gold' standard), to achieve a ninety percent accuracy in diagnosis of PSP, for a diagnosis today still has to be made by observation of clinical symptoms. For, although Magnetic Resonance Imaging and other tests can support a diagnosis, there is as yet no diagnostic marker for PSP. This remains a major concern to us and possible solutions are discussed further later in this Chapter under the heading 'Earlier and Better Diagnosis', the theme of our Fourth International Medical Workshop.

At that time, PSP prevalence estimates ranged, across the UK's population, from the extremes of one thousand to ten thousand living PSP patients.

In 1998 and 1999, Professor Niall Quinn, a leading neurologist and member of our Medical Advisory Panel, and Dr Anette Schrag, both based at the Institute of Neurology in Queen's Square, carried out a prevalence study of the number of living patients with PSP and with Multiple System Atrophy in Greater London[13]. Their findings were of a prevalence of PSP of between six and seven

10. *Professor Andrew Lees and Dr Sue Daniel 1997*
11. *I Litvan , L Golbe et al SPSP/NINDS Criteria*
12. *Dr David Williams*
13. *Prevalence of Progressive Supranuclear Palsy and multiple system atrophy: a cross-reference study The Lancet Vol 354*

per hundred thousand of population, an order of magnitude considerably greater than previously found in smaller surveys carried out previously around the world.

Our 'spot check' survey and a subsequent meeting of neurologists at the Institute of Neurology led Professor Andrew Lees, as Chairman of our Medical Advisory Panel to approach the Association of British Neurologists and the British Neurological Surveillance Unit to seek their support for a nation-wide epidemiological survey into PSP, subject to funding and a suitable Project Coordinator being found.

Dr Uma Nath, then a Registrar at Newcastle General Hospital, volunteered for this role, and was invited by our Medical Advisory Panel to present to the Trustees of The PSP Association her proposal to research the prevalence and incidence of PSP across the UK. She also recommended the creation by the Department of Health of a National register for PSP and related neurodegenerative diseases. However, there has been little progress on this, mainly due to lack of funds and insufficient detail on underlying causes in death certificates, on which she has reported separately[14].

We recognised that without funding from The PSP Association, this survey would not take place. After an outstanding presentation in 1999 by Dr Nath to our Trustees, the Association agreed to sponsor her two year Project to establish the prevalence of PSP and to estimate the number of living patients across the UK, at a cost to the Association of £93,000 over two years – to us, then, a massive sum!

Dr Nath had proposed a clever 'Russian Doll' Project, to start in October 1998. Her plan involved three concentric studies within the overall Project. The 'inner ring' would cover Newcastle-upon-Tyne itself in considerable detail, the 'middle ring' being the North East of England, where a population of some 3.5 million would be sifted to identify PSP patients and an 'outer ring' of the whole of the UK, based on 'follow up' reports over a given period from the British Neurological Unit.

This Unit, supported by the Association of British Neurologists, had agreed to distribute 'reporting cards' to some 310 UK Neurology Consultants and 100 specialist registrars. All identified PSP patients would be asked to enter the study. Those willing, or their carers, would be asked to complete a questionnaire about their family history. Blood samples would also be requested. National databases of atypical parkinsonism and medical records would be searched. Clearance by the Medical Ethical Committees concerned would be obtained before the Project began. Valuable epidemiological and statistical support was generously to be provided by Professor Yoav Ben-Shlomo in Bristol and Professor Richard Thomson in Newcastle.

The study would provide insight into the observed geographic clusters and levels of under diagnosis and misdiagnosis, engender awareness of PSP, particularly within the relevant medical profes-

---

Nov 20 1999 A Schrag et al

14. Dr Nath et al Population Based Mortality and quality of death certification in PSP. J. Neurol. Neurosurg. Psychiatry 2005;76;498-502

sion, and collect associated data for subsequent trials and research projects.

However, its main aim would be to produce as clear a picture as possible of the prevalence and incidence of PSP across the UK. Having heard Dr Nath's presentation, Trustees enthusiastically supported the Project, which began that October.

With immense thoroughness and impressive support from surgeries, Dr Nath, after two years intense research, arrived at a prevalence figure for Newcastle. This was age adjusted and compared with the results of her middle and outer ring studies. The results were extrapolated, giving a final figure across the UK of a prevalence of 6.4 and incidence of 5.3 per 100,000 of population. It was encouraging to find that her figures so closely matched those of Dr Anette Schrag's for Greater London. Dr Nath's findings were published in 'Brain 2001'[15].

These figures are now accepted across the UK and published in Appendix 3 (Incidence and Prevalence of Neurological Conditions) of the Neurological Alliance's Paper 'Levelling Up' dated May 2002[16]. They confirm PSP to be at least as common and, most neurologists would agree, at least as nasty as its far better known cousin Motor Neurone Disease.

Our third International Medical Workshop was once again held in the State Rooms at Stowe School and once again attended by distinguished delegates from around the world. We held this Workshop jointly with the Alzheimer's Disease Society with a focus on the related biology of these two, and other closely related, neurodegenerative diseases. The common thread was the 'Tau' protein. All these diseases can be grouped as tauopathies. Research into the Tau gene and the neurofibrillary tangles of Tau in the brain in these diseases is discussed later in this Chapter. It once again proved to be a very popular and well attended Workshop.

Our fourth Workshop, held in 2003, our last at Stowe, focussed primarily on earlier and better diagnosis of PSP. It was another very enjoyable and successful Meeting, concluding that, without earlier diagnosis, the treatment of PSP, when it becomes available, could come too late to reverse the damage already caused by the disease's progress. Some of the arguments debated then are outlined below.

Over the decade, there has been an acute shortage of neurologists across the UK. It takes ten years to train a neurologist and the UK is still near the bottom of the European league in terms of numbers of neurologists per million of population. Those with real expertise in PSP can be counted on one hand. By no means all PSP patients are even seen by a neurologist and not all geriatricians have had the expertise to make, with the necessary high degree of accuracy, this difficult diagnosis.

Some doctors, geriatricians and even neurologists still feel that it is better not to give a diagnosis of PSP – effectively a death sentence, if there is any doubt in their mind and sometimes, we suspect, even when there is not. "What is the point", they perhaps say, "in worrying the patient and their family with a diagnosis, for which we can offer no effective treatment and no cure, particularly with

15. *Brain (2001) 124, 1438 – 1449 Uma Nath et al*
16. *Nikki Joule 'Levelling Up' May 2002*

older patients? Better just to leave it as a form of Parkinson's Disease or parkinsonism". Questionnaires to afflicted families, however, reveal how desperate people are to know the truth, however awful. Also, as the search for a cure for neurodegenerative diseases continues to close in on possible treatments, it will become essential to 'catch the disease early'.

Clinical trials of drugs to treat such diseases will therefore require earlier and more accurate differential diagnosis, if the right disease is to be treated in time. Reversing the damage caused by the disease is likely to be much harder than slowing or stopping it. Today, the clinician can only observe the symptoms displayed by the patient, which often reflect a variety of possible diseases. Without a test to confirm a tentative diagnosis, it is easy to see the difficulties of 'getting it right' and the pressure to wait for further confirmatory symptoms to appear.

Furthermore, today a scientist carrying out research of any sort on living patients diagnosed as having PSP, can still only be sure of the accuracy of their given diagnosis after the patient's death, by pathological examination of donated brain tissue. It therefore still remains possible that some of the living patients diagnosed as having this disease and consequently included for such research, have, in fact, not 'got' PSP but a related neurodegenerative disease, thereby undermining the statistical results of the research.

A genuine differential diagnostic marker would resolve these major problems in PSP. For all the above reasons, The PSP Association has strongly supported and sponsored research with potential to identify such markers.

Serial Magnetic Resonance Imaging (MRI) scanning was first performed in Alzheimer's Disease by Professor Nick Fox in 2000. Dr Dominic Paviour became the first PSP Research Fellow at the Sara Koe PSP Research Centre and from 2003 to 2005 carried out similar research, involving a MRI scan every six months on selected volunteer PSP patients.

Using sophisticated computer software, a brain image scanned six months after a previous scan, by using this technique, can be orientated to align exactly with the first; and the differences in shape and volume in key areas of the brain over this period then be calculated. These differences represent the progression of the disease. The location and level of loss provides strong clues as to the disease and its rate of progression. The conclusion of this project was that serial scanning could support a clinician's diagnosis, but it was not yet sufficiently clear cut to become a diagnostic marker. However, it was recognised as an extremely valuable tool for measuring the rate of progress of the disease and hence the effectiveness of a drug in a clinical trial.

New scanners, with more powerful magnets, like the one at Queen Square (some three times as powerful as a normal hospital scanner), enable much sharper images to be seen, though the size of the area to be scanned is too small to be used on living patients. However by comparing the images obtained on pathological brain tissue by this scanner with post mortem pathological staining images, a much clearer and sharper picture can be obtained and indication of damage deduced.

Dr Luke Massey, who has been carrying out this research under the direction of Professor Andrew Lees, is optimistic that, as new scanning techniques and more powerful magnets become available for use on living patients, the information provided (knowing where to look and what to look for) will enable *in vivo* scanning to become a true diagnostic marker, confirming and enabling earlier diagnosis.

Such scanning techniques will, for example, be able to compare changes in water levels in key structures of the brain, including in the midbrain, the brain stem and the subthalamic nucleus, (using serial diffusion weighting imaging techniques on hospital scanners). It is already clear that this technique will improve markedly serial scanning's ability to measure the rate of progress of PSP and monitor the effect of drugs in slowing this rate.

In 2004, Professor Gavin Giovannoni proposed the use of proteomics (the study of proteins) to try to identify whether or not subjects with PSP have a characteristic or unique profile of proteins in their spinal fluid or blood. If so, this profile could then be used as a diagnostic marker to enable clinicians, with a simple spinal tap, to confirm a tentative early diagnosis. This proposed protein research fitted in well with other research into treatment and cure outlined below, focussing on the Tau protein. The PSP Association duly sponsored Connie Luk, a Postdoctoral Research Fellow, working under Professor Giovannoni's direction, to undertake this three year research Project to start in the autumn of 2005. Her initial aim was to build up, using spinal fluid (obtained by lumbar puncture) and blood samples from patients and from controls, a central resource for PSP and related disorders to form a 'spinal fluid resource bank' at the Sara Koe PSP Research Centre, alongside the brain bank there.

Using a rapid and simple laboratory test that is based on antibody and antigen interactions called ELISA (Enzyme Linked Immunosorbent Assays), the relevant levels of Tau in post-mortem brains were ascertained. The levels of four-repeat were found to be present at high abundance in affected areas of PSP brains compared to healthy control brains where the level of three-repeat was higher. The practicality of a similar test in complex biological fluids such as cerebrospinal fluid (CSF) is still being assessed. Such a sensitive and specific test would be extremely valuable to help neurologists identify PSP patients by simply carrying out a lumbar puncture procedure.

The growing need, referred to earlier, for a research centre in the UK to provide a focal point for medical research into PSP in the UK with close links to research across Europe (and also to research in the USA and other countries around the world), and to encourage more government support and funding for such research, led to plans to create such a centre in London.

On 17th April 2002, our Patron, HRH The Duchess of Gloucester, GCVO formally opened what was happily to be called the Sara Koe PSP Research Centre (SKRC) alongside the Queen Square Brain Bank, at 1 Wakefield Street, London, as part of the Institute of Neurology. Our President, Field Marshal Lord Bramall, Lady Bramall, Professor Richard Frackowiak, then Dean of the National Hospital and Institute, our new Chairman of Trustees, Sir Michael Carleton-Smith, other Trustees, Professor Andrew Lees, Director of the Reta Lila Weston Institute of Neurology (RLWI),

Professor John Hardy, then a Director at the National Institutes of Health, Professor Tamas Revesz, Director of the Institute's new Pathological Laboratory, and members of the Koe family (in force!) were present.

This event was the culmination of some detailed joint planning between the Dean of the Institute, the RWLI, Professor Andrew Lees and the PSP Association to establish in one place in the UK, such a PSP Research Centre. Following our planning, Trustees had offered an annual sponsorship of a minimum of £100,000 toward the SKRC, in the form of basic salaries of a research fellow, an administrator and research technician, the costs of which the RWLI generously agreed to match.

Ms Susan Stoneham was appointed to be the Administrator of the Centre. Her role includes coordination with The PSP Association over brain donations, new research applicants and other matters of joint interest. She is a very empathetic and helpful person, and soon became a good and immensely supportive friend of The PSP Association. The PSP Association sponsored Research Technician is Mrs Linda Parsons (nee Kilford), recently married, who has also been enormously supportive to our cause. Our current Research Fellow, Dr Luke Massey, took over from Dr Dominic Paviour in this role, continuing the high standard set by the latter.

The Centre, the first such Centre in the world, in addition to its research role, provides a focal point for PSP research in Europe, and also provides a dedicated PSP Reference Library and DNA and Brain Resource Centre interlinked with the new Queen Square Brain Bank (QSBB), accommodated in the same building.

In 2005, 1 Wakefield Street had a one million pound building refurbishment, following which Professor Lees' Directorate moved in to bring together the Centre, the Brain Bank and the RWLI. This provided critical mass and a coordinating centre for the rapidly expanding research into PSP across the world.

Much of this research requires pathological examination of brain tissue and hence the importance of donation of people's brains after death. The Queen Square Brain Bank and other such Banks, which hold such tissue, are absolutely crucial to research across the neurodegenerative disease field. Without the generous and pre-planned brain donations from not only those diagnosed as having one of these diseases but from 'controls' - those with healthy brains - research into these diseases would be severely hampered. For the bulk of research into neurodegenerative diseases perforce has to rely on the study of pathological brain tissue.

Professor Tamas Revesz is a neuropathologist. As such, he leads the QSBB team alongside the SKRC at 1 Wakefield Street. His Directorate's research focus is on the pathology of neurodegenerative diseases. His responsibilities as Director of the Queen Square Brain Bank ensures that:

~ all donated brains are examined to confirm diagnosis,

~ next of kin in due course are given the confirmed diagnosis,

~ donated brains are stored appropriately and

~ authorised researchers applying for diagnosed brain tissue for their research, once their research has been cleared by the relevant ethical committees, are appropriately supplied.

As mentioned earlier, pathological examination is the gold standard of diagnosis of PSP. From the above, it can be seen that his work had been pivotal in research sponsored by The PSP Association.

Another Centre of Excellence, which coordinates closely with the SKRC and Queen Square Brain Bank has been in Newcastle-Upon-Tyne.

Professor David Burn is based there at Newcastle University's National Institute for Ageing and Health. He is an infectiously enthusiastic, thorough and impressive neurologist recognised internationally. He has also amazingly – considering his prodigious workload – found time to train and to run to raise money for The PSP Association's research in marathons and cross country events, including the New York Marathon, watched by your Author. He is a member of our Medical Advisory Panel and yet another very good friend of the Association.

Professor Burn has, over the life of the Association, coordinated a range of research into PSP sponsored by The PSP Association, including that of Drs Uma Nath, Adam Zermansky, Naomi Warren and Margaret Piggott, covering the prevalence, risk factors and natural history of PSP, as well as research into the effect of this disease on the cholinergic and acetylcholine receptors of the brain. This important research has involved pathological examination of key areas of brain tissue to identify the damage caused to specific neurons in specific areas, matching this with observed symptoms in living patients.

In addition, he himself has taken on cutting edge research into PSP, including, as the UK's lead, the exciting ongoing planning of a joint Lithium Trial on PSP patients near selected centres in the USA, in the UK and in Canada, outlined at the end of this Chapter.

Going back to the early days of the Charity, 1994 saw the astonishing exponential growth in scientific understanding of the mechanisms of the brain and the role of genes in neurodegenerative diseases. The publication of the coding of the Human Genome, with its twenty three pairs of chromosomes, each of which made up of a long string of DNA (the twisted helix ladder with its rungs and coded letters), particularly spurred on the latter.

The DNA code is made up from permutations of just four letters or 'nucleotides' in the DNA alphabet (a bit like the twenty six in ours). These four alone are sufficient to do the astonishing (miraculous) job of providing the coded messages contained in the DNA for the selection of the necessary amino acid from a choice of twenty to instruct the production of all the proteins required to design a human being!

The sequence of these letters, unlike in a clone, varies along the coding from individual to individual. Most such variations seem to have no apparent consequence, but some, it is now known, can cause susceptibility to inherited diseases. Each variation is known as a single nucleotide polymorphism or SNP (happily pronounced 'snip' like 'a bargain' or perhaps more appropriately, what scissors do).

The publication of the make up of the Human Genome and, in 1999, of the first 'complete' chromosome sequencing, led to a rapid growth of research into the genetic components of neurodegenerative diseases. For the first time, scientists could access all of the contiguous genes and control sequences in a substantial fraction of the human genome. Some nine years later, this genetic research has provided exciting clues into the cause and mechanisms of such diseases, though, frustratingly, turning this knowledge into potential treatment and cure is proving much tougher. In PSP, there is certainly much greater understanding, but still uncertainty as to how and to what extent genetic and environmental factors combine to contribute to its onset.

The remarkable progress over the last decade in understanding the mechanisms of PSP and related diseases, both in protein and genetic terms, has been driven by the close collaboration between dedicated scientists across the world, working together and coordinating their research planning and findings. The Internet has made a major impact on this. Whereas a dozen years ago, a scientist would seek to find time to read up on colleagues' work often over the weekend, usually some time after publication, now they exchange emails on the subject at the time their research is in progress, on a day to day basis.

It is acknowledged here that the somewhat arbitrary selection of research into PSP and related diseases discussed and acknowledged in this book, grossly understates the enormous effort that has gone into such research and into neurodegenerative diseases since the start of the 21st Century, and its coordination around the world. The vital input from those like Professors Andrew Lees, Lawrence Golbe, John Hardy, Irene Litvan, Yves Agid, Nigel Leigh, David Burn and Eduardo Tolosa – to name but a few – and other leading scientists in this process are widely recognised and hereby acknowledged. For the record, those scientists who carried out research sponsored or part sponsored by The PSP Association from its registration until 2008 are listed, with a brief description of their research, its length and its cost at Appendix 1 to this Chapter.

From the perspective of this book, however, further discussion about research into the cause, treatment and cure of PSP is broadly split into that involving genes and that involving protein.

Genetic research carried out by Dr Huw Morris and Dr Rohan de Silva, assisted by Kate Strand, under the direction of Professor Andrew Lees, sponsored by The PSP Association and 'picked up' by the Medical Research Council, has played an important part in international research into the genetics of PSP.

Dr Morris' research, in his pilot genetic study, in 1997, and subsequently Dr de Silva's research, both initially sponsored by the PSP Association led to each receiving an award of a three year's Research Fellowship by the UK's Medical Research Centre Advisory Panel.

Their work in the UK has been coordinated closely with that being undertaken by Professor John Hardy (later to become a Member of our Medical Advisory Panel) and his team at the National Institutes of Health in the USA and with other related international research into genetic susceptibility in PSP. All this research has focussed on the 'Tau' gene. There is now strong evidence that this gene on Chromosome 17q21, or a nearby genetic factor, is associated with an increased susceptibility to the disease.

In 2004, The PSP Association also sponsored Dr Pau Pastor to carry out, in the USA, a two year project involving genetic analysis of this region in familial frontotemporal dementia and in sporadic tauopathies, including PSP. His research, coordinated with other work there, identified specific combinations of variants associated with these diseases and in some way involved in their progression.

The Tau gene has two main variants or haplotypes, referred to as H1 and H2. Research into these variants indicated that only those people carrying the H1 variant are susceptible, for carrying this genetic variation is a necessary but not sufficient requirement to have PSP[17]. However, over 50% of the UK population carry the H1 haplotype gene, so there must be further genetic and/or environmental factors actually triggering the disease in those susceptible. Recent research also indicates that the H2 variants are themselves neuro protective.

CurePSP and The PSP Association are currently jointly sponsoring Dr Richard Wade-Martins at Oxford University to carry out research, using a molecular genetic technique, better to understand the differences in the way H1 and H2 produce Microtube Associated Protein Tau (MAPT). This will lead, in turn, to a better understanding of the molecular and genetic mechanisms of PSP. Meanwhile, The PSP Association is sponsoring a further piece of research by Dr Morris into the HI haplotype, to examine, in post-mortem brain tissue, the control of the expression of the Tau gene.

In the USA, an exciting new $1.2 million Project is being sponsored by CurePSP to search the whole human genome for defects relating to PSP and identifying those defects most amenable to treatment interventions. This research will use a gene chip which can test, for one individual, over half a million SNPs, from which the location of each are precisely known on its chromosome. This method can provide incriminating evidence in whole genome analysis, so that the exact nucleotide sequence in the suspect area can be ascertained to identify the functions that are going wrong in PSP. Similar technology has applications for a very wide range of diseases involving genetic susceptibility.

This next paragraph seeks to sum up in layman's terms what we now know, as a result of researchers' work, about the pathology of PSP; what causes it and why. Biologically and pathologically, PSP, in its disease mechanism, has more in common with Alzheimer's than Parkinson's Disease. As in Alzheimer's, the post mortem brain of a PSP patient contains protein aggregations, or neurofibrillary tangles. The Tau in such tangles has an excess of phosphate. It is described as being hyperphosphorylated. These tangles destroy the neuronal communication pathways and can be seen in microscopic examination of brain tissue. The two main variations of the Tau protein are three repeat (3R) and four repeat Tau (4R) (this refers to whether a particular piece of genetically-coded protein is included or excluded from the final protein product). International research in which Drs Rohan de Silva and Dr David Williams, in particular, were involved confirmed that the four repeat

17. Dr Huw Morris PSP Bulletin Autumn 2006

Tau (4R) was more abundant in PSP patients brains than the three repeat Tau (3R).

In 2003, Dr Diane Hanger's research at King's College in London identified the enzyme (Glycogen Synthase Kinase or GSK-3) and its involvement in the hyperphosporylation of Tau in Alzheimer's Disease. This discovery led pharmaceutical companies to invest large sums in potential therapeutic interventions based on a search for compounds to provide treatment for Alzheimer's, by modifying the actions of this enzyme.

In 2005, Dr Hanger and her assistant, Selina Wray, undertook a similar three year project of research into the neurofibrillary tangles of the protein Tau and its over-production of phosphate in PSP, jointly sponsored by The PSP Association and the Medical Research Council. This research has now been extended for a further year. Their successful purification and separation of a fragment of hyperphosphorylated Tau specific to PSP may provide clues as to what happens to Tau in PSP and the related molecular progression of the disease, with the possibility of finding a compound to modify the actions of the enzyme, GSK-3 on PSP, thereby reducing phosphate levels in the Tau and moderating the disease itself.

We held our fifth International Medical Workshop on Friday, 8th July 2005 at the National Hospital for Neurology and Neurosurgery. Its focus was on PSP as a test bed for neurodegenerative disease-modifying treatments. We changed both the venue and day to suit those international delegates who wished to combine a weekend's shopping and the bright lights of London with the Workshop.

Our plans, however, were, like many other plans that day in London, severely disrupted by the unexpected but, in hindsight, inevitable albeit devastating terrorist attack there, which took place on the Thursday morning, 7th July, the day before our Workshop, a stone's throw from the Hospital.

The front entrance to the nearby President Hotel, into which we had booked the majority of our delegates, was sealed off by the police for twenty four hours. By then, many of the eighty odd delegates from around the world were closing in on London and the hotel; some had already arrived at Heathrow and other air and rail heads in the region. Others were still at overseas airports, waiting to depart or still back at home, having been advised by their Government on no account to travel to London.

On hearing the news, many rang our 'headquarters', wondering if we still planned to go ahead with our Workshop. Despite such devastating and chaotic circumstances, it was difficult to say 'no, we did not', although medical teams, including speakers at our Workshop, were, at that time, being deployed to King's Cross and to Tavistock Square, where the bus had been blown up. Although everyone was very aware of the priority of helping victims and dealing with the crisis itself, we were not keen to cancel at this stage, particularly with so many delegates already en route. We therefore opted not to make a final decision until the picture was clearer. Whilst we postponed this, to us important, but, in the scheme of things, rather minor decision, the remarkably efficient, coordinated and organised reaction from the police, the transport services, the ambulances and the doctors, resulted in order being gradually restored.

Professor John Hardy is an outstanding English neuroscientist, who was attending this Workshop as the leader of a team of neurologists at the National Institutes for Health in Washington, USA. Behind his laid back and light hearted style and casual dress (as seen in the rare photograph of him in this book, actually wearing a tie in honour of our Workshop!), there lies concealed a remarkably sharp and perceptive brain.

John had flown in to London the day before. Having arrived at Queen Square, he sized up the situation, made a quick reconnaissance, and then telephoned me, still at our Offices in Wappenham, to recommend that we went ahead with the Workshop, with delegates we had booked in to stay at the President Hotel gaining access there through a tunnel from the Square into the back of the hotel he knew about from the years he had previously worked at the Institute of Neurology, to which he has recently returned.

Later that afternoon, we therefore decided to go ahead as planned, and were delighted to find the next morning we still had at least an eighty percent turnout, despite the inevitable cancellations following the murderous attack and the chaotic scenes which followed. Sympathetic delegates were determined not to let this stop the Workshop being a success, despite the inevitable confusion and 'ad lib' and 'ad hoc' arrangements. This was much appreciated by the harassed organisers, though movement was difficult as there were no buses, underground trains or taxis on the day of the Workshop. (Fortunately, the walk from the President Hotel to the Theatre in the Hospital was only a couple of hundred yards).

Professor Colin Blakemore, Chief Executive of the Medical Research Council (MRC) and by then one of the distinguished Vice Presidents of The PSP Association, set a good example by doggedly walking a couple of miles from Park Crescent to the Lecture Theatre to give the opening address. We then heard some impressive and encouraging presentations, followed by positive and forward looking proposals. It proved in the end to be a very harmonious, successful and happy Workshop. Sharing the pain of 9/11 and 7/7 had not only brought the transatlantic partnership closer together, but our Workshop was also energised and strengthened by the sympathetic reaction of other delegates from around the world.

Scientifically, it addressed the cogent theme, carefully listened to and absorbed, we hoped, by pharmaceutical representatives present, that PSP was, because of its brutally rapid progression and its remarkable biological similarity to Alzheimer's and other tauopathies (with the formation in the brain of neurofibrillary tangles of tau), an ideal test bed for research into potential disease moderating drugs for such diseases; and that therefore such trials were worthy of their investment.

Our Sixth Medical Workshop took place again in Queen Square in London, in much more peaceful surroundings. It was very well attended and followed by a very enjoyable dinner at the prestigious Rifles Club in Davies Street.

This Workshop broadly followed the theme of the Fifth, but its focus was more on specific clinical trials of drugs for treatment of PSP. There were several drug candidates considered. The tentative plan for a clinical trial of Lithium, about which more later, was particularly exciting.

During the Workshop, Professor Nigel Leigh, from King's College, London – another good friend of our Association – briefed delegates on the first major drug trial into PSP. This was called the NNIPPS Trial (Neuroprotection and Natural History in Progressive Supranuclear Palsy and Multiple System Atrophy). In 1999, he had applied for funding from the European Union for a clinical trial of Riluzole, a drug manufactured by Aventis (which had been demonstrated as being modestly beneficial for Motor Neurone Disease patients) for patients across Europe with PSP and MSA.

Funding of some two million Euros was granted by the EU for this major clinical project, which included a planning phase, a patient recruiting phase, the Trial itself and post Trial analysis, which took place in Germany, France and the UK, over the next six years. Its challenging objectives were to assess the therapeutic efficacy and safety of the drug, to construct and validate diagnostic and severity staging and to measure the quality of life of patients, their cognitive functions and the economics of these diseases.

The trial itself covered a three year period from July 2002 to November 2005. It was an ambitious and complex double blind, placebo controlled, stratified, parallel group study of the efficacy and safety of Riluzole for some 400 PSP and 400 MSA patients, who volunteered from across the three countries concerned.

Two further projects were introduced to the trial (1) to look into the genetic aspects (involving blood sampling to provide DNA for further research) and (2) to seek to obtain offers of pathological samples (involving examination of brain tissue after death) of PSP and MSA patients. All NNIPPS patients were accordingly invited to volunteer for these extra research projects, but obviously not obliged to do so. The genetic project built up a bank of genetic samples which will help in further research into the cause of these two diseases. The pathological aspects were seen to be crucial to confirm retrospectively the diagnosis of those volunteering as incorrect diagnoses would invalidate results. There were thirteen Regional Centres across the UK, with some 105 of the large number PSP patients who volunteered from the UK being accepted as being within the trial criteria.

The NNIPPS Trial was the largest and most systematic clinical trial and prospective study of the natural history of PSP and MSA to have taken place to date into either of these two related diseases. Although the trial itself finished in December 2004, patients continued receiving the drug on an open label basis, whilst data was checked and the outstanding mass of information collected and collated. This took longer than expected with three different countries involved and the need for meticulous checking of all data gathered from some 636 patients with PSP and 404 with MSA. It proved to be an enormous task. Finally, in the winter of 2006, the analysis was completed.

Sadly, Riluzole was not found to have any positive effect on survival and was not therefore going to be a useful drug for people with PSP or MSA. However, from the huge amount of data collected from the trial, much valuable information was derived. It provided unique insights into clinical aspects of PSP and MSA; it raised awareness within the scientific community of these two diseases; it led to the development of a rating scale; it monitored change in mobility over time and provided much information on psychological changes, quality of life and the costs to service providers and families during the course of living with these diseases. The NNIPPS Trials also laid a sound basis for future clinical trials. The considerable efforts of the patients, nurses, doctors and scientists involved were certainly not wasted.

Inevitably, because of the close historic and symptomatic ties between PSP and Parkinson's Disease, other clinical trials and treatments which have been tried or shown to be effective in the latter have been trialled or looked at closely as to their effectiveness in PSP.

Electroconvulsive Therapy (ECT) is effective in improving the motor symptoms in Parkinson's disease, possibly by sensitisation of dopaminergic and noradrenergic systems. There have been several reports of ECT treatment in people with PSP. In general, the treatment has had no clear benefit and may be associated with temporary worsening of some features, including mental function and swallowing.

Functionally blocking overactive parts of the brain in Parkinson's disease by the implantation of electrodes into key areas (known as deep brain stimulation, DBS) has led to dramatic functional improvements for those with this disease. Prior to the availability of DBS, neurosurgeons used to achieve the same effect by freezing or burning the same brain areas, to render them non-functional. The latter procedure (suffixed with '– tomy') was, of course, irreversible. A small number of people with PSP have undergone one of these procedures, called pallidotomy. Sadly this was without significant clinical benefit.

One of the problems with both DBS and lesioning of the brain in PSP is that the pathological process in this disorder is more widespread than in Parkinson's disease. Thus, if one imagines trying to get a message down a telephone line, correcting the wire being down between two telegraph poles may work for Parkinson's disease, whereas in PSP there are other breaks in the wire, in locations that we do not yet fully understand.

Undeterred by this, other brain targets for DBS are being considered in PSP. One of these is a long thin collection of grey matter in the brainstem called the pedunculopontine nucleus (or PPN). Early work in animal models and in a few people with Parkinson's disease suggests that stimulating this site at a certain frequency *may* improve axial problems and walking. Since this area is known to be badly affected in PSP, the PPN may be a DBS target worth evaluating further.

Taking pieces of a person's own adrenal glands and transplanting them into basal ganglia of the brain could, in theory, lead to the local production of dopamine by the transplanted cells. This procedure has been reported in only three PSP patients. The transplants had very limited benefit and were associated with a number of post-operative complications.

No foetal transplants have been undertaken in PSP. Since these transplants involve the use of dopamine-producing cells, one would predict that they would have limited or no benefit, given the more widespread neurotransmitter involvement in PSP, and the lack of response to levodopa drugs in this disorder. The same would therefore hold true for stem cells, engineered to produce dopamine.

Legal and ethical issues surrounding cloning and use of adult or pluripotent embryonic stem cells in research and their ability, rather than potential, to treat or even cure neurodegenerative diseases like Parkinson's Disease and other life threatening diseases have become the subject of intense debate. Embryonic stem cells are master cells that can grow into any sort of tissue. Thus they have the potential - if not rejected by the body - to create replacements for cells that are lost or damaged. To avoid rejection, cloning is proposed.

Recent research undertaken in the USA using mice bred to develop the equivalent of Parkinson's Disease has involved the use of cloned cells cultured to grow into dopamine neurons. These then have been implanted in to the brains of mice, resulting in improvement of their neurological symptoms and with no signs of rejection of the transplanted tissue. However, the hope of the use of cloned cells as a therapy for Parkinson's Disease is today no more than that. It is at best some way in the future.

The possible use of stem cells in PSP, in research terms, still remains well into the future. There is no medically based evidence available today to indicate that this treatment would be in any way beneficial in PSP. There are considerable technical challenges as well as inherent medical risks in such treatment approaches that need to be overcome first. Sadly, there will always be, around the world, some who claim they can offer 'miraculous results or even cures' for neurodegenerative conditions like PSP. Such groups are regarded by the medical profession with scepticism, at best, particularly as their data is rarely, if ever published in reputable, peer-reviewed journals.

It can be argued that developing future treatments for PSP should not rely too much upon picking up scraps from the table of Parkinson's Disease approaches. Unravelling the cause of neurofibrillary tangles of Tau in the brain and reducing phosphate levels in microtubular scaffolding is seen as a much more realistic near term goal. Interventions aimed at the basic disease mechanisms in PSP (excessive deposition of Tau protein and novel treatments aimed at reducing the overproduction of Tau, or improving its removal), is considered by the majority of leading scientists in this field potentially a more effective way ahead. Anti-inflammatory drugs or agents that reduce excessive phosphorylation of the Tau protein (such as lithium) may also have therapeutic promise in PSP.

After some fourteen years of collaborative and coordinated research across the International Scientific Community into the cause and treatment of PSP since the formation of The PSP Association and its sister charity in the USA, the stage at last is now set for clinical research trials into drugs which might moderate the inexorable progress of this devastating disease. PSP afflicted families will inevitably remain desperate to try anything that might help – from their point of view, the risk of trials going wrong and drugs not working or even harming them are well worth accepting, if there is a reasonable chance of slowing or stopping the disease. However, seen from the viewpoint of those running such trials and from the viewpoint of ethical committees, trials have to be well designed, with full and proper safeguards.

With several possible candidate drugs in the pipeline, The PSP Association's 2007 International Workshop was a timely event to debate collaboration over such clinical trials and the way forward. From all the research already described in this Chapter, a clinical trial of a compound already cleared for human use that might inhibit the enzyme responsible for the overproduction of '4R' Tau in the brain, was favoured, providing the necessary dosage was acceptable to patients on whom the drug would need to be trialled.

In 2001, animal trials of mice in the USA had been carried out by Drs Mike Hutton and Karen Duff. They had successfully 'made' mice overproduce the Tau protein, and thereby demonstrated that these 'transgenic' mice consequently developed PSP 'look alike' symptoms. In post mortem examination, it could be seen that the mice had deposited tell-tale neurofibrillary tangles of Tau in their brains, indistinguishable from that found in PSP. By switching off Tau production, it had also been demonstrated that the mice then 'got better'.

This was important evidence, but not directly useful for human therapy, as genes can't just be switched on and off in living patients. However, further work showed that if the enzymes which overproduce phosphate can be inhibited in mice by a suitable compound – and lithium was shown to be one such compound - using which, the formation of tangles in mice could be prevented. However, mice are not men and lithium, although an approved drug, is a powerful and potentially toxic one and there was no certainty that PSP subjects, particularly older and more frail ones, could tolerate the necessary doses.

There was a constructive debate at our Sixth Workshop on the way ahead for such Clinical Trials. Several drugs, such as Lithium, Valproic Acid, Coenzyme Q10, Amantadine, Galantamine, Rivastigmine and Rember were considered to be possible candidates. Galantamine (from the snowdrop bulb) and Riverstigmine may alleviate memory loss by improving the acetylcholine system. However, they are both cholinominetics, very similar to Donepezil, already trialled with disappointing results under Professor Irene Litvan' direction. Rember or Methylthonium Chloride is the most recently included candidate. It has been found to dissolve neurofibrillary tangle of Tau in Alzheimer's with positive results.

In France, a small two year clinical trial supported by contributions both from the French PSP Association and from The PSP Association has begun, using Valproic Acid on sixteen selected patients.

In the USA, the UK and Canada, centres are volunteering to become sites in a joint Lithium Clinical Trial, sponsored by the National Institutes of Health (NIH) in the USA, with a modest contribution from our Association. The Trial is being coordinated by Professors Wendy Galpern at the NIH in the USA, Tony Lang in Canada and David Burn in the UK. At the time of writing, a protocol

1. *New York Skyline*

2. *Central Park '06*

3. *John Sutton & Peter Garvey from Integro*

4. *The 1st PSP Association New York Marathon '96*

1. *'The Cousins' at the New Zealand Golf Club*

2. *David Clews at Coventry Golf Club*

3. *Kevin Keegan & Friends support PSP*

1. *Our 1st Magnolia Ball - Stowe School*

2. *At the Ball*

3. *Falstaff!*

4. *The Royal Green Jackets' Buglers*

5. *Martyn Downer in action*

1. *Dr Malherbe after the London Marathon*   2. *Crossing Tower Bridge*   3. *Final Stages - The Embankment*

4. *View from the ABPI*

1. *At the PSP HAC Ball London*

2. *Guests at the Ball*

3. *At the Roulette Wheel*

1. *A Presentation at the Medical Workshop*

2. *A Distinguished Gathering after the Workshop*

3. *The Third International Medical Workshop at Stowe*

1. *PSP Quiz Evening at Bush House*

2. *Carol Service at St Clements - Eastcheap '03*

1. *Alex Shaw (Sara's Cousin)*

2. *Nicholas Shaw*

3. *Jinnie Harman (née Shaw)*

4. *Elaine Colton*

5. *The Algarve Ride '07*

1. *Cycling in the Atlas Mountains*

2. *The Marathon des Sables*

3. *With a trophy!*

4. *Full pack!*

5. *At the finish!*

1. *Lord Coe (Seb) welcomes guests*

2. *Seb's table at the Riverbank Marquee*

3. *The PSP Association Stakes*

1. *Windsor Races - Joan Tice presents the Cup*

2. *Seb with Frankie Dettori*

3. *Frankie celebrates!*

1. *Lady Juliet Townsend welcomes HRH*

2. *Jane Hardy is presented to HRH*

3. *Michael Koe escorts HRH around the new PSP Offices*

4. *HRH greets the Mayor of Towcester*

1. *1 Wakefield Street '06*

2. *The Sara Koe PSP Research Centre (SKRC)*

3. *Planning the SKRC*

1. *Mary Baker*

2. *Professor Andrew Lees*

3. *The opening of the SKRC*

1. *Neurologists at the 2003 Workshop*

2. *The National Institute for Neurology & Neurosurgery*

1. *A chat over coffee*

2. *Enjoying a drink after the Workshop*

3. *The Sixth Workshop in London*

4. *Dinner after the Workshop*

has been written and collaborative sites and ethical approval are being sought. The six months trial due to start in 2008, will have a clear focus on tolerability, but changes in the rate of progress of the disease over the period of the trial will also be measured to provide information regarding the biological effects of the drug and some limited preliminary data regarding possible clinical benefits.

If lithium is shown to be adequately tolerated by this study, it is expected that the trial would provide sufficient data to proceed with a larger placebo controlled trial to determine drug efficacy in slowing the progress of PSP.

Cutting edge research into the astonishingly complex mechanisms of the human brain lies at the frontiers of science. Such research has been compared to that into the origins of the universe, such as at CERN where protons are accelerated to near the speed of light to collide, emitting particle such as quarks and possibly even the 'God Particle' 'Higgs' Bosun', and simulate the first few milliseconds after the 'big bang' some 13.7 billion years ago. However each new discovery seems to lead to further complexity with the final truth still just around the corner.

Treatment and cure will be found one day in the reasonably near future for PSP and other related neurodegenerative diseases, but neither easily nor quickly. However, those neuro scientists who have dedicated their lives to unravelling the cause and finding disease modifying treatments can truly be proud of the progress they have made.

Research into PSP sponsored by The Psp Association
From 1995 - 2007

1995/1996 – Dr Peter Pramstaller (Italy/Austria) [under the direction of Professor Andrew Lees] **- a six month PSP Research Fellow. His work included:**
~ collection and collation of all existing research into PSP worldwide and recording this on Reference Manager
~ questionnaire on familial Susceptibility
~ design of a Neuro-Epidemiological Project in the Tyrol (NEPT) (ongoing)
~ research into Post-Encephalitic Parkinson Syndrome and PSP
~ the effect of PSP on the bladder and sexual dysfunction

Cost to the PSP Association   £12,000

1996 – First International PSP Medical Workshop or Brain-storming Meeting
The 'Way Ahead' for Research into PSP, attended by some 60 of the World's leading neurologists. Held at Marie Curie Research Institute in Surrey, UK.

Cost to the PSP Association   £12,000

1996/1998 – Dr Thomas Bak [under the direction of Professor John Hodges]

A longitudinal study into the neuro-psychological, neuro-psychiatric and behavioural effects of PSP on patients across the UK (at Cambridge - Joint Award with the University of Cambridge). Dr Bak was awarded a Research Fellowship appointment at the Cognitive & Brain Sciences Unit in Cambridge as Research Assistant to Professor John Hodges.
Cost to the PSP Association   £20,000

1997/1999 – Dr Huw Morris [under the direction of Professor Andrew Lees]
Research into genetic susceptibility in PSP at the Institute of Neurology in London [Dr Nick Wood, Principal Investigator]. In 1998 Dr Morris was awarded a 3-year Research Fellowship to continue his research by the British Medical Research Council (MRC). The MRC awarded him a 3 year funded Fellowship to continue this work in the second year of his PSP Association grant, so he has completed some five years on this important research.
Cost to the PSP Association   £50,000

1999 – Second International PSP Medical Workshop
For PSP, MSA and CBD, the related so-called 'ugly cousins' of Parkinson's Disease. Held at Stowe School, Buckinghamshire, for some 70 of the World's leading neurologists.
Cost to the PSP Association   £12,000

1999/2000 – Dr Uma Nath [under the direction of Dr David Burn]
Nationwide 'Russian Doll' epidemiological and PSP prevalence study at RVI, Newcastle upon Tyne. This was supported by the Association of British Neurologists and co-ordinated across the UK by Professor Andrew Lees with PSP Association input. It confirmed Dr Anette Schrag's work the previous year, in the Greater London area, that PSP was an order of magnitude more common than previously assessed, with a prevalence of at least 5 per 100,000 of the population. Leading neurologists now believe there could be as many as 10,000 living patients across the UK.
Cost to the PSP Association   £90,000

1999/2000 – Dr Rohan de Silva [under the direction of Professor Andrew Lees]
Sequence analysis of genomic tau and Messenger RNA at the Institute of Neurology. Following up Dr Morris' work, Dr de Silva was appointed and remains as a PSP Research Fellow.
Cost to the PSP Association   £40,000
Continues as a PSP Research Fellow 2001 / 2004, but sponsored by the Reta Lila Weston Foundation.

1999/2001 – Dr Tamas Revesz & Tammaryn Lashley
Tau protein and Messenger RNA research [directly consequential of Dr Huw Morris' research] at the Institute of Neurology. Dr Revesz worked in a team with Dr Sue Daniel and Professor Brian

Anderton on this research. Tammaryn Lashley was his Research Assistant. She is now continuing her work on PSP in the USA, having gained her PhD in London with this work.
Cost to the PSP Association £60,000

Dr Anette Schrag [under the direction of Professor Niall Quinn]
Phase 1 – 1999/2001
The design of a 'Quality of Life' Instrument for medical professionals on assessing the effects of PSP on patients' and carers' Quality of Life. Phase 1 2001/2002
Cost to the PSP Association £11,000
Phase 2 – 2001/2002
'Quality of Life' in PSP Instrument at the Institute of Neurology. A continuation of previous research over a much larger number of PSP patients, designed to put together an internationally recognised Instrument.
Cost to the PSP Association £15,000
Phase 3 – 2002/2004
'Quality of Life' Instrument at the Institute of Neurology. A continuation of previous research over a much larger number of PSP patients, designed to put together an internationally-recognised Instrument. This research is now in its final stage. PSP patients and their carers within the Association across the UK recently completed a further series of questionnaires designed to authenticate the wording of the new instrument.
Cost Sponsored by the US SPSP £45,000

2000 (March – June) – Dr Chloe Stallibrass
Alexander technique and its effect on a PSP patient
Cost to the PSP Association £3,500

2000/2001 – Dr Roberta Vitaliani [under the direction of Professor Scaravilli]
Investigation of spinal cords of patients with PSP. In Italy and at the Institute of Neurology in London.
Cost to the PSP Association £5,000

2000/2003 – Dr Adam Zermansky [under the direction of Dr David Burn]
Using the mass of data collected in Dr Uma Nath's epidemiological study, Dr Zermansky carried out a three-year Natural History, Risk Factor and Magnetic Resonance Spectroscopy study into PSP at Newcastle upon Tyne. This continuing study used data collected by Dr Nath to look at geographical clustering, familial linkages and environmental factors in triggering PSP.
Cost to the PSP Association £113,000

2000/2004 – Alice Everett, Linda Donald & Gini Hearn

Assistants to Dr Thomas Bak in continuation of the longitudinal study into the effects of PSP on behaviour at the Cognitive and Brain Sciences Unit in Cambridge. Alice Everett moved to another appointment at the end of the year 2000, and Linda Donald took over. She was followed by Gini Hearn at the end of 2001

Cost to the PSP Association   £80,000

2001 – Third International PSP Medical Workshop

A joint Workshop with the Alzheimer's Disease Society for leading neurologists from around the World, focusing on tau and amyloids. This two day Workshop took place at Stowe School, Buckinghamshire, in October 2001.

Cost to the PSP Association   £15,000

2001/2002 Dr David Nicholl [under the direction of Professor Robinson]

DNA Bank in Birmingham, tied in with the Riluzole Trial

Cost to the PSP Association   £3,500

2001/2003 Dr Bas Bloem [under the direction of Professor Andrew Lees]

The initial study was followed by a second international study into falls in PSP/MSA and PD. The initial study involved research into fractures from falls in PSP, with questionnaires sent to afflicted families within the PSP Association across the UK.

Negligible costs to the Association

2001/2004 – Professor Nigel Leigh

A trial of the effects of Riluzole – a drug, which was beneficial in Motor Neurone Disease – on PSP and MSA patients. The trial, sponsored by the European Union, will cover Germany, France and the UK, and a total of 400 PSP and 400 MSA patients, looking at a wide range of related subjects concerning patient care.

Paid for by EU - support only required from the PSP Association

2001/2004 – Dr Dominic Paviour [under the direction of Professor Andrew Lees]

Further research into genetic susceptibility in PSP as a three year Research Fellow at the Rita Lela Weston Research Foundation. This may be extended for a further year.

Cost to the PSP Association   £117,000

2001/2004 – Dr Justo Garcia de Yebenes

Familial research into PSP in Spain. A re-submitted research proposal. Some of this special Spanish family have now been assessed in recent PET and MRI scanning in London, the latter done by Dr Paviour.

Cost to the PSP Association   £13,200

2001 / 2006 - Dr Peter Pramstaller

GenNova - a Project based on NEPT in the Tyrol, sponsored, over 5 years, by Local Government in Italy.

No cost to the Association - liaison only

2002 onward – Sara Koe PSP Research Centre (SKRC)

Officially opened by HRH The Duchess of Gloucester, GCVO, in April 2002.

Objectives include:

- ~ Coordination of PSP Research worldwide
- ~ UK PSP Research Coordination Centre
- ~ Acceptance of PSP brain donations
- ~ Linkage to the Queen Square Brain Bank
- ~ A Resource for the pathological research
- ~ Holding other archive material concerning PSP

Cost to the PSP Association:

FY 2002/03	£80,000
FY 2003/04	£107,213
FY 2004/05	£115,788
FY 2005/06	£122,049
FY 2006/07	£128,704
FY 2007/08	£133,262

The PSP Association has committed to sponsor the SKRC £135,000 in 2008/09 and £140,000 in 2009/10.

2003 – Fourth International PSP Medical Workshop

A workshop for leading Neurologists from around the World, focusing on earlier and better diagnosis of PSP. This one day Workshop was held at Stowe School in July 2003.

Cost to the PSP Association   £12,000

2003 / 2005 – Dr Pau Pastor, Dr Alison Goate & Prof Eduardo Tolosa

Genetic analysis of 17q21 region of familial fronto-temporal dementia in sporadic tauopathies. Work undertaken in the USA and Spain.

Cost to the PSP Association   £24,000

2003/2005 –Dr Naomi Turner [under the direction of Dr David Burn]
A continuation of the work undertaken by Dr Adam Zermansky, including 2 year Clinical Magnetic Resonance Spectroscopic and Neuro-chemical studies in PSP
Cost to the PSP Association   £30,000

2003/2004 – Dr Thomas Bak [under the direction of Professor John Hodges]
Continuation of work in Language, Semantics, Visuo-spatial functions & behaviour in PSP. Contribution of cortical & sub-cortical pathology. This work was previously funded by the MRC.
Cost to the PSP Association   £20,000

2004 –Dr John Steele
Cataloguing & repatriation of research material from Guam to be lodged at The Sara Koe PSP Research Centre. Lecture Tour on PSP to major UK teaching hospitals. The extra cost would go towards a video production, which he would coordinate, under the direction of Professor Andrew Lees (UK) and Professor Lawrence Golbe (USA) for neurologists in the UK and USA.
Cost to the PSP Association   £14,000

2004/2005 - Dr Naomi Warren [under the direction of Dr David Burn]
Year 2 October 2004 to October 2005. Completion of her research into the cholinergic system and subtypes of receptors in PSP.
Cost to the PSP Association   £44,600

2004/2005 - Dr Dominic Paviour [under the direction of Professor Andrew Lees]
A grant for an additional year in Serial MRI Scanning to support the clinician in differential diagnosis of PSP.
Cost to the PSP Association   £47,700

2004/2007 - Dr Rohan de Silva [under the direction of Professor Andrew Lees]
Kate Strand Technician. A comparative pathological biochemical and genetic classification of classical and atypical PSP brains.
Cost to the PSP Association   £82,700

2004/2007 – Dr Diane Hanger
A three year grant starting in October 2004 investigating the link between tau phosphorylation sites and PSP – Selina Wray Technician.
Cost to the PSP Association   £33,300

2005 - Extension of work by Dr Thomas Bak
Research into the behavioural effects of PSP on PSP patients.
Cost to the PSP Association £5,000

2005 - Fifth International Medical Workshop
A Workshop for leading Neurologists from around the World, focusing on as a 'Test-bed For Neuro-degenerative Disease-modifying Treatments'. This day was held in Nottingham on 8th July 2005.
Cost to the PSP Association £12,000

2005/2006 - Dr Huw Morris (in Cardiff)
A one year grant covering the employment of a Grade D Technician researching into suppression of tau transcription as a possible therapeutic intervention in PSP.
Cost to the PSP Association £31,700

2006/2008 – Dr Margaret Piggott
A two year grant covering with a start date of January 2006 researching into cholinergic dysfunction resulting from degeneration of the pedunculopontine tegmental nucleus in PSP: A major determinant of clinical features?
Cost to the PSP Association £79,336

2007 – Extension of work by Dr Margaret Piggott
To extend the Project by three months to the end of June 2008 on 'Cholinergic dysfunction resulting from degeneration of the pedunculopontine tegmental nucleus in PSP: A major determinant of clinical features?'
Cost to the PSP Association £9,148

2007 – Sixth International Medical Workshop
A workshop for leading Neurologists from around the World, focusing on 'Clinical Trials in Progressive Supranuclear Palsy'. This was held in London on 27th June 2007.
Cost to the PSP Association £10,500

2007/2009 – Dr Luke Massey (under the direction of Dr Tarek Yousry)
A two year grant starting in January 2007 into High-field, quantitative MRI in PSP: Post-mortem characterisation of the SN, STN and the pedunculopontine nucleus.
Cost to the PSP Association £132,475

2007/2008 – Dr Diane Hanger
To extend Selina Wray's project for a further year into tau fragments starting from October 2007.
Cost to the PSP Association   £32,200

2007/2009 – Dr Huw Morris (in Cardiff)
A two year grant starting in March 2007 into Analysis of tau gene (MAPT) expression in PSP.
Cost to the PSP Association   £93,119

2008 – Dr Pascal Derkinderen
A one year grant into a "A randomized placebo-controlled trial of valproic acid in patients with progressive supranuclear palsy (PSP)" starting January 2008 (Approximately £20,000)
Cost to the PSP Association   £13,500

2008 – Professor David Burn
A two year grant towards the cost of a proposed Lithium Tolerability Trial, which has not yet started.
Cost to the PSP Association   £12,552

2008/2010 – Dr Richard Wade-Martins
A two year grant starting in February 2008 into Haplotype regulation of alternative splicing at the MAPT locus.
Cost to the Association   £25,000

Total Research   **£2,124,046**

6. *Engendering awareness*

To be aware of, appraised, cognizant or conscious of something is clearly a prerequisite to effective planned action or reaction. Without such awareness by the relevant health and welfare professionals, by decision makers and by sufficient numbers of the general public, proper recognition of a disease, equitable funding for research into its treatment and cure and the necessary care and support for its victims is unlikely to be provided.

Before the turn of the Century, awareness of neurological diseases still remained astonishingly low and that of PSP pretty well non existent, not just within the public arena but also amongst health related decision makers and, dare it be said, even amongst the relevant medical and welfare professions themselves. Neurological diseases remained the 'Cinderella' of medicine and PSP, if mentioned, was generally considered, by the former, to be a rare form of Parkinson's Disease and by the latter as a form of parkinsonism. Few had heard of Progressive Supranuclear Palsy, and fewer still had experience of knowingly dealing with patients facing its progressive symptoms.

Historically, however, there is strong evidence that this disease existed at least as far back as the nineteenth century, when Charles Dickens[18] vividly described an encounter with a man in a public house bearing all the symptoms of this disease:

"A chilled, slow, earthy, fixed old man. A cadaverous man of measured speech. An old man, who seemed unable to wink, as if his eyelids had been nailed to his forehead. A old man whose eyes—two spots of fire—had no more motion than [sic] if they had been connected with the back of his skull by screws driven through it, and riveted and bolted outside, among his grey hair. He had come in and shut the door, and he now sat down. He did not bend himself to sit, as other people do, but seemed to sink bolt upright, as if in water, until the chair stopped him."

However, PSP was not formally recognised as such until the nineteen sixties and even today still lingers under the shadow of Parkinson's Disease.

Because there was little or no research into its treatment, there seemed to be, from the viewpoint of those on the 'receiving end', little apparent interest in this neglected but devastating disease. There was, in fact, not a lot that the medical profession could offer even in the way of symptomatic treatment, so:-

"Come back in six months and meanwhile here are some pills that might help" (which help in Parkinson's Disease but often don't and can actually be counter productive for PSP).

and/or

"Here is the business card of The PSP Association. Get in touch with them and they will explain more about the disease and tell you what help they can offer,"

seemed to some Carers of those with PSP to be many 'professionals' standard response to their

18. *Page 195, 'The Idle Apprentice' Charles Dickens*

concerns.

However, by then, a dedicated group of international neurologists were already seeking to change attitudes and increase awareness of PSP. Professors Irene Litvan and Yves Agid's book[19] about new clinical and research approaches to PSP, refered to in the previous chapter, opens with a 'wake up' call:-

"Until recently, Progressive Supranuclear Palsy (PSP), otherwise known as Steele-Richardson-Olszewski syndrome, has been considered an obscure neurological disorder. This view has changed with the recognition that the disease is more common than previously thought."[20]

Much has changed over the last fifteen years. PSP is now known to be at least as common and, most neurologists would agree, at least as nasty as its far better known cousin, Motor Neurone Disease, though there is a still a long way to go before it is treated equally supportively and until early and accurate differential diagnosis of PSP is able regularly and appropriately to be given.

Recent research confirms that PSP has a prevalence of at least 6.4 per 100,000 of population in the UK, and, as quoted Professor Lawrence Golbe in his Layman's Guide to PSP in the late nineties, there are *"at least 20,000 living patients with PSP across the USA"*. There is no reason to believe that there is not a similar prevalence of this disease in other countries around the world. Certainly in other parts of Europe and in Japan, PSP has been diagnosed in numbers comparable to the UK and, as mentioned elsewhere in this book, these prevalence figures are likely to be very conservative.

A priority for our Association has therefore been to raise the level of awareness of PSP to that necessary to ensure that patients and their carers receive an equitable share of available care and support and that our Government's funding for research into its cause, treatment and cure is made more proportional and equitable, in balancing it with other calls.

Raising awareness is, in financial terms, 'open ended', both in the size of 'investment' that can be made and the difficulty in predicting the return on a given investment.

We have focussed our strategy and available funds within the Association on engendering awareness of PSP amongst four key groups:

~ relevant health and welfare professionals
~ politicians and other decision makers
~ our subscribers,
~ the general public at large.

There is, of course, considerable overlap between these groups, as there is between awareness and fundraising. Some of the major events we have organised have had the raising of awareness amongst influential people present as at least an equal priority to that of directly raising funds. For example, our golf competitions do not raise large sums themselves, but have led through contacts to substantial donations toward cutting edge research into PSP.

19. *Progressive Supranuclear Palsy – Clinical and Research Approaches by Irene Litvan and Yves Agid 1992*
20. *Matsuo et al 1991*

Raising the level of awareness amongst relevant health and welfare professionals remains closely linked to the day to day work of The PSP Association's Care and Support Team; and the provision of information and support by the Charity across the health and welfare sector. Our tactic here has been to combine a 'top down' with a 'bottom up' approach.

Our targets from within the NHS have included neurologists, ophthalmologists, geriatricians, doctors, nurses, therapists (speech, language and physio) and dieticians. Within the Welfare Sector, we have focussed on nursing and care homes and carers working under the Social Services remit. It is particularly in this area that the tragic effects of lack of knowledge and lack of appropriate care for people with these little known neurodegenerative diseases are most keenly felt.

In our 'top down' approach, we have looked for opportunities to publish articles and/or make presentations to umbrella organisations, such as the Association of British Neurologists, the British Geriatricians Society, the Royal College of Nurses, the National Association of Neurological Occupational Therapists (NANOT), The Royal College of Speech and Language Therapists, the Associated Chartists and Physiotherapists Interested in Neurology (ACPIN) and the Association of Parkinson's Disease Nurse Specialists (PDNS). These umbrella groups represent the 'front line' of neurologists, nurses and therapists supporting people with PSP.

With the help of the Educational Broadcasting Trust, we organised, with CurePSP and with the direct support and involvement of leading neurologists from both the USA and UK, a fifteen minute DVD put together in London entitled 'A Physicians Guide to PSP'. We circulated this on a very wide distribution to all the above umbrella groups and other interested parties. We also sent copies to our emerging European sister charities. CurePSP circulated it similarly across the USA and Canada. Altogether, well over twenty thousand copies were sent out (some ten thousand each, by us and by CurePSP and several thousand by the German and French PSP Associations) across Europe and the USA to provide a credible reference guide for those professionals who might need it.

We joined Alliances including the Neurological Alliance, the Association of Medical Research Charities, the Genetics Interest Group, the National Council of Palliative Care, the Neurological and the Long Term Medical Care Alliance. It has been difficult, with every aspect of our Charity growing fast, to find enough time to become as involved with these key umbrella groups as we would like and do more than just write the occasional article or give a presentation when invited to their meetings. There is still considerable scope for further 'top down' awareness raising, but a fair appraisal might read *"good progress has been made to date with limited resources, but could do more"*.

Turning to our 'Bottom Up' approach, the Charity began in 2000 to recruit 'Regional Development Officers' (RDOs) across the country to help raise the level of knowledge of PSP and our Charity's work amongst health and welfare professionals, at grass roots level. Our first Regional Development Officer was Maureen Fowler, who lives in the East Midlands and had worked in the Patient and Public Involvement Forum and British Lung Foundation there; so knew her way around her region! She was, we quickly found out, an experienced and highly capable operator. We invited her to cover the whole East Midlands (plus some adjacent territory to the North!) and to network with relevant health and welfare professionals there. Her primary task was to raise awareness, with a secondary role of supporting our Local Support Groups, within her region.

With the frustrating delays, discussed earlier, in the long awaited implementation of the National Framework for Neurological Conditions (the NSF) and its eleven Quality Requirements, her third role was to monitor its progress (or, as sadly is the case to date, lack of!) in Primary Care Trusts, within her region.

As part of her primary role, she organised Regional Information Seminars (RIS), involving presentations by our Nurse Specialists at meetings to which relevant health and welfare professionals were invited from across the region. During this period, it became clear that the Government and Department of Health were decentralising and standing back from overseeing the implementation of the NSF, passing the buck to PCTs to br monitored by Health Commissions. This raised the importance of our regional awareness building role; and the need for them to network with PCT members. As we raised more funds, we expanded our development service, with the aim of covering the whole country, as and when we could afford to.

We next recruited, in East Anglia, Gina Rutterford, who lived near Peterborough, and who had worked with Sarah Wollaston at the charity Deaf Blind UK. She quickly proved to be a 'ball of fire' in developing contacts and networking in her region. Early on, she organised a hugely successful first joint Regional Information Seminar (RIS) with other neuro degenerative disease charities – so successful that some applicants to attend had to be turned away for lack of room!

Our third appointment, Michael Scott, had considerable experience in a similar field to Maureen Fowler, and took on West Midlands, where he lived; and responsibility for North Wales.

Our fourth and fifth appointments covered Scotland and Northern Ireland. We had been concerned by the large number of misdiagnosed or undiagnosed patients there must be there, based on the number joining our Association– seriously below the levels our prevalence figures from these parts of the UK would suggest – and alarmed that many of those joining our Association from these parts of the country were not receiving the information and support they needed.

We recognised that the title and role of these appointments would need to be changed, particularly in light of the devolution of health responsibilities to Scottish and Welsh Parliaments and that we should consider registering as a Scottish Charity as well as an English one. For, although the Quality Requirements of the NSF remain valid across the whole of the UK, the implementation methodology and the actual process varies considerably.

We also recognised that it would be unacceptable to describe Madeleine Quine, who took up this post covering the whole of Scotland and Sandra Campbell in Northern Ireland as our 'Regional Development Officers', so we dropped 'Regional' from their titles and our RDOs became Development Officers or DOs.

Madeleine, a good friend, based in Edinburgh, had helped organise our Local Support Group there. She became DO Scotland and had soon set up two more Local Support Groups and actively networked with other health professionals across the country.

Sandra Campbell, whose Father had died of PSP, became DO for Northern Ireland and soon was galvanising Stormont into action (pictures of Martin McGuiness cowering in the corner as she berated him on lack of funds and support for PSP patients). She also offered her support to PSP patients in the South, attending our Local Support Group Meetings in Dublin as well as in Belfast. Our sixth DO was Kathy Miller- Hunt, whose Mother had PSP. Kathy took on the South West of England and South Wales.

Already, she, and our other DOs, have successfully and imaginatively networked in with other medical professionals, raising sharply the profile of PSP at local, regional and national levels and providing essential information and support both for professionals and for afflicted families, within their areas of responsibility. They have made an impressive impact; and will fit in neatly with the new Regional Neurological Alliances being set up by the Neurological Alliance across England, with financial support from the Department of Health.

The remaining three DO's to complete our cover of the UK are planned to be recruited as soon as the Association's budget allows, with priority in the South Central England. (At the time of writing, the Association has just recruited Lisa Goodridge for this post. She is a nurse and her Father -in-Law had PSP).

A crucial aspect of our Awareness Campaign has been to seek to move neurological diseases in general and PSP in particular up the political agenda and engender greater awareness amongst decision makers of the plight of afflicted families and the need for more research funding in this area of medicine. To this end, we set up, in 2004, an All Party Parliamentary Group to lobby our cause.

Such a Group requires a Member of Parliament as Chair and a specified number of MPs from either House for each Party. Tim Boswell Esq., our local MP and a good friend, generously agreed to become Chairman of our APPG. Lord Coe was again very helpful here, both in lobbying friends and becoming one of our two Vice Chairmen. Frank Dobson MP, whom we had recently briefed at the Sara Koe PSP Research Centre, became the other. Nikki Joule, who had considerable experience in this field and in the workings of Parliament, agreed to act as our APPG Coordinator and advisor. Between us, we sought to 'recruit' new Members and soon had the requisite number to become a registered Group and hold our first Meeting, at which Professor Martin Rossor gave a helpful brief on the commonality and inter-linkage between neurodegenerative diseases. The Group also addressed concerns about the care and support available within the National Health Service for those with neurological conditions, particularly those with PSP.

Nikki Joule had been for several years the Policy Officer of the Neurological Alliance before setting up as an independent Consultant and provided a useful bridge between us and them. The Neurological Alliance (NA) itself brings together more than fifty 'Third Sector' organisations, which collectively represent ten million people with a neurological condition. Its aim is to ensure that everyone with a neurological condition has access to the best information, support and care – no matter where they live in the country. It also campaigns over issues of concern to its member charities and is able obtain direct access to Ministers and other decision makers in the Department of Health (DoH) to lobby for its causes, but, at the time of writing, still does not have its own APPG and therefore has to rely on those of its members to act collaboratively on its behalf over common issues – in our view an unsatisfactory position, which we hope to see changed!

A key issue for all members of the NA had been the lack of any visible progress in the implementation of the NSF for Long Term Neurological Conditions. Delegation without clear cut direction has led, we believe, to inaction by overstretched and reorganised Primary Care Trusts. This failure is disadvantaging people with neurological conditions.

It was of great concern to the NA as a whole that the DoH decision further to decentralise responsibility for implementation of the NSF from the DoH to Primary Care Trusts was not supported by work to raise the profile of the NSF with providers, nor by work to ensure that the commissioners, managers and professionals purchase and provide high quality joined-up services for people with neurological conditions.

Our APPG accordingly invited Professor Ian Philp, the Department of Health lead for this NSF, to present on its progress. He gave a useful update on workforce development, commissioning guidance and plans for auditing, benchmarking and the inspection of services provided by the implementation of the NSF. He explained that there were minimum resources committed to the NSF at the Department. Decision making and funding had been delegated to PCTs and key levers for implementation were through local networks and local accountability networks. Tim Boswell, MP as Chairman wrote to the Secretary of State to express the concern of our APPG about this and to seek early implementation of effective plans to monitor the progress of the NSF.

Members of the PSP APPG, together with the members of the Multiple Sclerosis, Motor Neurone Disease and Epilepsy APPGs then met with Stephen Ladyman MP, the Minister then responsible for the NSF for Long Term Conditions and expressed deep concern on behalf of all members of the Neurological Alliance about lack of funding to improve neurological services and about shortages in the neurological workforce.

The Minister said there was enough money in the system to implement the NSF and that it would lead to an increase in the number of neurologists and other neurological staff, although it was pointed out that the former take up to ten years to train. Letters from the Chairman of our APPG about this and about Continuing Care for PSP patients were duly sent to the Secretary of State and added to the pressure on her to take necessary action.

Across the UK, in addition to the need to raise awareness amongst the relevant health and welfare professionals and decision makers, there is a clear need to do so amongst others with influence in the health debate and, more widely, amongst the general public, since their support is crucial to better services and to the essential funds we need to achieve our objectives.

Our Subscribers, (mainly, as one would expect, people with PSP, their carers, afflicted families, friends and supporters and health and welfare professionals) have played a key role in raising awareness of PSP and of the work of our Association amongst the general public. Many of them have touching stories, with often moving, painful and distressing accounts of their fight with this implacable disease, told with humour and courage; and local newspapers and television have been interested in such stories, right from the setting up of our Association. There was, for example, a long and moving article in the Independent newspaper, written by a freelance journalist about Sara, written whilst she was still alive[21]. The response to appeals made later by the Charity to our families and other subscribers to approach the media with stories of their battles with PSP has been tremendous and has done much to raise awareness amongst the general public at large.

Sponsored challenges, like Marathons, particularly those run to raise funds for research in support of relatives or friends with this disease, make good articles that local media readily publish. Increasingly, national newspapers have health supplements, which have become popular reading.

Our newsletter, as mentioned in Chapter 4, goes out three times a year to all our subscribers. It includes an editorial by the Chief Executive, a Research Section updating readers on current research, particularly that sponsored by the PSP Association, a Section on Care and Support, a Section on Awareness and Fundraising and a Miscellaneous Section. Since 1999, these newsletters have included colour photographs of activities in which subscribers and the Association itself have taken part. Copies of each newsletter were circulated, to doner trusts and other doners, to selected health and welfare professionals and others as well as to subsribers. Since 2008 our newly named PSP Matters has been copied on the PSP Association website and circulation accordingly restricted mainly to subscribers (to cut mounting costs).

Since straight spending to achieve a sufficient level of awareness amongst the general public is not an affordable option for smaller charities like ours, inventive, proactive and reactive PR to raise awareness amongst the general public have all been essential tools in our strategy. The use of media opportunities, of fundraising events, of individuals with influence and of celebrities are discussed briefly within this Chapter, together with the overlap between fundraising and awareness. Trustees of The PSP Association continue to place raising awareness in its broader sense as our overall top priority in respect to its objectives to achieve our Mission.

The setting up of The PSP Association's website has already briefly been discussed in Chapter 4. It had become an increasingly important awareness tool, but to remain effective needed to be made ever more interesting, imaginative and colourful; and more regularly updated with news and other useful information. Technology in this area moves fast and keeping 'up to speed' is expensive but essential to maintaining audience interest. We recognise it as a crucial tool in the provision and updating of information and news; and of raising awareness of PSP and the Charity across the world. We accordingly appointed Rebecca Benney as our Director of Information and PR in 2006 and allo-

21. Roger Dobson, The Independent, 9th August 1994

cated funding, within limited resources, to bring and keep it up to the mark. Rebecca is accordingly in the process of unfolding, with outside website advice, a major update and re-design of the site.

Our website's Discussion Forum, on which readers can post queries and responses from reader feedback, is not only extremely helpful to afflicted families, some of whom have nowhere else to turn, but continues to raise awareness on a 'drip feed' basis.

Nonetheless, without greater public awareness of this disease, we will never reach our objectives. Some of the answers to the public awareness dilemma lie in imaginative use of the media. An ideal public awareness raising target, for example, would be a major television 'soap' in which a character developed PSP. This route has been successfully adopted by several larger charities supporting well known diseases, such as cancer, working closely with the adopted programme. However, for the rarer diseases, it is extremely difficult to 'break in' and interest the programmers (the catch twenty two is that until the pubic are aware of a disease, they are unlikely to identify with a soap character going down with it) and to date the Association has not succeeded in doing so, though we continue to try. As this is being written, a BBC documentary called 'A short Stay in Switzerland' about Dr Anne Turner, who had PSP and opted for euthanasia there, is programmed to be shown later this year.

We have held opportunity 'talk ins' with radio stations, with excellent returns for investment. We sought help, for example, from a media marketing company in London, who arranged for a 'Coe and Koe' programme (in which The Lord Coe KBE (Seb) and I spent a morning answering questions on PSP. Seb, as would be expected, handled with consummate skill those questions slipped in about 2012 rather than PSP! We faced a battery of questions from presenters of eleven radio stations, slotted in at ten minute intervals over a couple of hours, during which period some eight million listeners heard the questions asked and our responses. We judged this to be a very cost effective albeit exhausting way of raising awareness!

Unsurprisingly, today, one of the most effective ways of raising awareness of a disease is through a celebrity who either has the disease or has a close relative with it. Dudley Moore's courageous declaration in 1999 that he had PSP and media coverage both in the USA, where he was living, and in the UK made a tremendous impact on awareness of this disease around the world. Even so, many newspapers wrongly reported he had a form of Parkinson's Disease and, as during the last five years of his life he lived in the USA, the impact of his illness and untimely death received wider publicity over there than in the UK. During this period, however, he came over to the UK to receive his CBE from HM The Queen and the public were shocked to see the deterioration in his physical appearance due to this devastating disease.

More recently, former Daily Mail newspaper columnist Nigel Dempster's diagnosis as having PSP and his subsequent death from it in 2007, was reported in national newspapers and television and also made a major impact across the UK in raising awareness of the disease. Soon after diagnosis, he generously agreed to take part in a short and moving video about how he was coping with

PSP, produced professionally by Nick Crean and Associates; and shown first at The PSP Association October Club Fundraising Dinner at the Savoy in 2004, described in the next Chapter.

The impact of other celebrities, or relatives of celebrities, including the actress Gemma Craven, whose father died from PSP, in raising awareness of PSP and about our Charity amongst the general public are also mentioned elsewhere in this book. Despite this celebrity 'boost' , ask the 'man on the street' whether the initials PSP mean anything to him and he is still more likely to say 'Play Station Portable' than Progressive Supranuclear Palsy. Whilst Motor Neurone Disease is now pretty well known and feared across the UK, our disease continues to remain tucked away in medical manuals.

So there is still a lot of work to be done in raising awareness of PSP, before it becomes a household word, and, more importantly, before afflicted families receive the care and support they need and sufficient funds flow into research to find the cause, effective treatment and cure of this devastating neurological disease.

Turning to relevant professionals and decision makers, a charity's campaign to raise awareness of can be pre-budgeted and pre-costed in forward planning. Returns on such an investment are, however less easy to measure. Effectively, in our case, output has to be assessed by seeking to quantify, in financial terms, resulting improvement in the standard of health care of patients.

Raised awareness levels amongst the general public is crucially important, but also not readily measurable. For example, if the cost of hiring a PR company, or directly placing an advertisement is the input, how do you assess the output? A financial guide to such investment in the general public might be:

"Put in as much as you can afford to and make the best assessment you can on whether the awareness you raise is worth it. Your return on investment will come largely from an increase in the numbers of people who donate toward your work or toward research you sponsor".

Raising awareness amongst the general public by The PSP Association has therefore tended to be largely reactive, taking advantage of opportunity (although proactive events, such as our Magnolia Day, have been, if not easily measurable, seemingly remarkably successful). We have sought, without the expenditure of large sums in advertising, to ensure that the acronym PSP triggers in peoples' minds this devastating disease and its implications for afflicted families. Branding, logos etc are, of course, important tools to help raise such awareness.

However, our pre planned or proactive awareness raising has mainly been limited to that linked to fundraising, such as that by our subscribers or from an event. For example, we invited to each of our Windsor Race Evenings some one hundred and fifty to two hundred influential guests, including celebrities. Awareness was engendered not only amongst these guests but, through the 5000 or more race cards, through our banners, through the public tannoy announcements and through the sponsored races, read, seen, and heard by the some 20,000 people at the races. These included information about PSP, what these initials stand for, the underlying disease, the suffering it causes and the Charity's work.

Returns from such pre-planned or proactive awareness activities are reflected in income from individual donors as well as from net income from the event itself, but this income needs to be split and allocated, as far as possible, between 'fundraising' and 'awareness' in any analysing process. This split of allocation can only be an educated guess. All this makes proactive expenditure of funds on raising public awareness often difficult to justify strictly in terms of financial returns, when an investment of £25,000 may provide a return of £40,000, but with an element of risk of achieving just a break even return or even worse.

There have been many different reactive opportunities to raise awareness of PSP through the media, one of the most recent being the opening of our new PSP Offices in Towcester, to which we invited our full hierarchy. We were absolutely delighted that our Patron, HRH The Duchess of Gloucester GCVO was able to come, as was one of our Vice Presidents, The Lord Coe KBE and our Lord Lieutenant Lady Juliet Townsend, as well as the Chairs of the Northampton and Towcester Councils and the Mayor of Towcester. The event took place on 23rd October 2007. The local media, including television (BBC Look East and Anglian TV) and newspapers (the Brackley and Buckingham Advertiser, the Northampton Chronicle and Echo and the Towcester Post) all contributed stories – some front page. The television coverage was particularly helpful and well presented and included a separate interview with a family in Milton Keynes, with husband and wife, the former having PSP.

The visit to The PSP Association offices included the arrival and presentations of VIPs to HRH in our car park at the rear of the building – fortunately the weather was kind for this as it would have all been an untidy squeeze indoors. After presentations down the reception line by Lady Juliet, HRH toured the offices and I was able to present staff, including our new about-to-be Chief Executive, Jane Hardy, at their desks, whilst Nurse Specialist Maggie Rose gave other VIPs a brief about PSP and our Charity in our Conference Room.

HRH then joined other guests in the Conference Room for further briefings on the progress of the Charity by John Chandler, our then Director of Care and Support and by me, before showing the seven minute video of Nigel Dempster. But the highlight of the visit was the unveiling of the plaque commemorating the opening of our new Offices, by HRH, who then gave a short but moving address to which our Chairman of Trustees, Sir Michael Carleton-Smith responded. It proved to be an uplifting and happy visit and a fitting start to the next step in the Charity's growth and future; it also neatly coincided with my hand over of the day to day running of Charity to Jane Hardy, and shortly thereafter take over from Sir Michael Carleton-Smith as Chairman of The PSP Association.

Events leading up to the setting up of the Charity, its organisation and its objectives have been described in these first seven Chapters. Its growth towards its objectives and goal has been entirely dependent on funds so generously donated. Fundraising has been the key to our growth. The next Chapter accordingly addresses this vital aspect of our work.chapter 7

7. *Fundraising*

Early efforts

Our early fundraising endeavours were probably typical of a small new charity. Shortly after Sara's Memorial Service, our first major fundraiser, in April 1995, involved my four sons, who had been devastated by her illness and death, running together (at the start anyway!), in the Flora London Marathon, as a small tribute to her, to help raise funds for our new Association. Those with any links with the Koe family, including from the Army and from across Northamptonshire and London (where all four then lived) were ruthlessly targeted! Through the generosity of our friends and relations, they thereby raised over £10,000 and set the pattern for future PSP Association focus on running events and Marathons.

Generous family and friends also found themselves providing key initial support in the form of donations or sponsorship of mainly local events we then ran or took part in, such as 'go carting', clay pigeon shooting, Scottish Reels evenings, concerts and a Magnolia Day raffle. We also, thanks to the organisational support generously provided by Caroline Clews and her husband David, held our first PSP Golf Competition at the attractive Coventry Golf Course, which thereafter became an annual and still fast growing event (though now nearing full capacity, with some sixteen teams of four taking part!)

Our other early fundraising efforts included 'recruiting' runners to take part in marathons in London, New York and in Paris, in what are often inappropriately called 'fun' runs, and in other mainly local events. All these fundraisers were generously supported by our subscribers and their friends touched by PSP. Funds built up rapidly but so did outgoings. It was time for our fundraising to become more professional.

Sarah Wollaston, our newly recruited Director of Fundraising, proposed a more formal fundraising strategy for the Association and in examining this, we looked at our main income streams, which came from:-

~   our Subscribers, including in memoriam and legacies
~   fundraising events largely organised by the Association
~   events organised by others, in which we took part
~   appeals and the General Public
~   Donor Trusts and Corporates
~   Gift Aid, tax efficient giving and interest on capital and shares.

This Chapter, under these six headings, describes our progress in developing these fundraising streams and lessons learnt. We revisited this strategy in 2001, with advice from fundraising consultants, which led directly to the setting up our Major Fundraising Appeals Committee and a planned approach to the October Club, a prestigious City based group of philanthropic asset management executives, described later in this Chapter.

Fundraising by our subscribers, including in memoriam and legacies

Initially, the bulk of our subscribers were carers, often relatives of those diagnosed as having PSP. We had set a subscription of £15 a head per annum per subscriber across Europe and double this elsewhere, as a reasonable contribution to help toward our work. We raised this, in 2001, to £20 (but kept it at £15 for standing order payment as an inducement to use that means!). Anyone who felt they could not afford to subscribe just had to let us know and we would waive the fee, though in practice we very rarely had to do so. As numbers increased, not only was this subscription a useful and calculable income source (which, strongly encouraged by Gerald Kirby, our Financial Controller, increasingly came in through standing orders) but this process also enabled us to keep more accurate records of patients and carers joining the Association.

After we had 'declared' 8th April as our Magnolia or PSP Remembrance Day, we invited subscribers to hold events like coffee mornings to mark the day – or if it suited them better, at other times through the year. The response to this request was tremendous.

As the years went by, our subscribers showed greater and greater inventiveness in the variety of fundraising they took on for us, including auctioning paintings, school dress-down days, a cryptic quiz, an office display, a garden party, a bridge evening, a 100th Birthday Party, a Fashion Show (by Denners, the Department Store in Dorset), sales of work, various ethnic lunches, a second hand book sale (by Turville Books), a Christmas Charity Bazaar, a concert in Wales (aptly named 'Take Note'), a Mad Hatter's Tea Party, a sponsored parachute jump and a Boxing Day 'dip' in the North Sea in winter to name but a few. Captains' charity days at golf courses around the UK organised by subscribers' families were also popular and rewarding fundraisers.

Our subscribers (or other members of their families) also took part in a huge variety of athletic pursuits and challenges, including marathons, triathlons, biathlons, the Great Scottish Walk, the Devil's Gallop (a fourteen kilometre race across country near Liverpool), the British 10km Run, mountain climbing and a wide variety of other athletic pursuits, including sections of the Tour de France.

So many friends and relatives of patients offered to undertake such events that Sarah Wollaston, Rebecca Benney and Sarah O'Connor were almost overwhelmed at times in providing advice and support as numbers grew.

In 2003, Helen Barkshire's Mother, Daphne, had PSP. As the disease progressed, her Father found it increasingly difficult to cook appetising meals for her. What started off as a casual conversion about how Helen could help, ended up as a major Project! During the summer, she wrote to numerous Celebrity Chefs, explaining her idea for a soft food cookery book and seeking their support in offering recipes for easy to swallow, easy to prepare and deliciously tasting meals.

The response was overwhelming; and included recipes from Gordon Ramsey, Raymond Blanc,

Nigella Lawson, Lady Claire MacDonald, Mary Berry, Leith's School of Food and Wine, Delia Smith, the River Café and Hugh Fearnley-Whittingstall.

Helen, helped by a friend who did the beautifully sketched illustrations, then put together a soft food cookery book, which she entitled 'Under the Magnolia Tree'. The Charity covered her expenses in publishing and sold the book through its Bulletin newsletters, website and other literature. It is a delightful simply bound and illustrated book and at £8 including postage and packing, remains very good value. We have had three reprints to date and have sold well over 1,500 copies. These can still be purchased from The PSP Association, to which all profits go.

Our first Christmas Cards were painted by Christopher Miers and Alex Wyman; overprinted by Abacus Press and sold by us for a modest profit to our subscribers and their friends, mainly through our Autumn Bulletin each year. Even though heavy in administration and time, this 'toe in the water' exercise proved to be very popular, a useful fundraiser and an attractive way of raising awareness of PSP and of our Charity, through information printed at the back of the cards. We accordingly, as our staff grew in numbers, continued to offer a selection of Christmas Cards each year over the years, but with volunteers taking on the bulk of the growing administration of our distribution process.

It is perhaps not surprising, given the nature of the disease that the Association has benefited from a steady growth in donations given in memory of those who have died from PSP. We have always been at pains to stress that all such donations, if at all possible, are acknowledged personally and will be used solely for the purpose specified by the family. In recent years, the total value of such donations per year has averaged over £60,000 – a very welcome source of income.

The collection of such donations may be co-ordinated through the Funeral Director or through direct contact with the donors. Either method has both advantages and disadvantages for the Charity. If the Funeral Director is collecting the donations, it is much less likely that the Charity will receive name and address details of the donors which makes claiming Gift Aid a 'non-starter' and prevents the capture of information on such donors which might be of future benefit. On the other hand, the administrative burden is much reduced. Obviously, the reverse is true where donations are sent directly to the Charity. In order to try and maximise the benefit to the Charity, Gift Envelopes (which include a Gift Aid Declaration on the back) are now available for distribution at funeral or memorial services.

During the first 10 years or so of the Charity's existence, income from legacies was very modest. Indeed, over a number of years, it was nil. However, more recently this situation has altered dramatically and although it is impossible to 'budget' for legacies it is perhaps not unreasonable to assume that with greater awareness of PSP and of the Association, this change will continue. Of particular note have been very significant legacies from William Stanley Megenis (£500,000 received in late 2005) and Arthur Calver (£150,000 received December 2007-January 2008). Neither of these people were previously known to us, as neither had joined our Association, although both had a direct personal interest in PSP; Mr Megenis, as a patient, and Mr Calver, as the husband of a deceased patient.

It has always been acknowledged that 'marketing' the idea of legacies is a potentially sensitive subject. As a result, the Association has adopted a low key approach, with references to the subject in issues of our newsletters and a section on the website. A survey of our subscribers at the time was undertaken in late 1999 and of those who replied, most were receptive to the idea of including The PSP Association as a legatee.

In late 2007, the concept of Tribute Funds was launched by the Charity. The objective was (and remains) to establish an ongoing 'Memorial Fund' for an individual to which contributions can be added at any time, to mark significant dates or anniversaries. It is envisaged that once a certain threshold of donations (by value) has been crossed, a permanent visual memorial in the form of a commemorative plaque might be placed at PSP House.

Fundraising events largely organised by the Association

As a charity, we have organised or helped organise a wide range of events ourselves, the number and size of which have only been limited by our assessment of risk and by availability of resources. Such events are, of course, usually heavily demanding on time, effort and organisational capacity. (Care and Support and Research Events such as our Symposia and International Medical Workshops are described elsewhere, but they too have been demanding on what were then currently the same resources and therefore cut into time and funds available for other events, anyway until more resources became obtained).

Fundraising Events run wholly or in part by the Charity are described here in chronological order, selected from many the charity has run or taken part in, on the basis of interest, size and input effort. Our early events helped shape and evolve our fundraising strategy to enable the Association to progress toward its objectives.

On 16th July 1998, we took part in an inter-company go-carting event organised by Haines Watts, then our Auditors, at Whilton Mills near Daventry, open to local Northamptonshire Companies. The PSP Association, with little or no experience of go-carting, was encouraged by Haines Watts to enter a team, generously sponsored by the James Mackaness Charitable Trust. We were more than happy to have a go! In the event, we had a great deal of fun in our carts but came, despite our best efforts and some reckless driving by our younger members, last, by an undisclosed distance! For our largely family team was definitely not in the same league as the other semi professional cut throat go-carters, including the Jordan and Venture Capital Teams to name but two. It was, however, a very enjoyable if somewhat noisy summers' evening, raising a net £500, which at that time seemed quite a lot of money for us. As a bonus, it raised considerable awareness of PSP locally and no little amusement – *"That team comes from a Charity in Northamptonshire, which helps people with this brain disease, called Progressive Supranuclear Palsy – so that's what PSP stands for. I hope they are better at looking after people with this disease than driving go-carts!"*

A year after our Grosvenor Inaugural Reception, described in Chapter 3, we organised our second high profile event – a Magnolia Ball in the State Rooms at Stowe School. To take this on, we set up a small but influential committee, with London and Northamptonshire membership, each member committing to bring a table of ten. The setting lent to a romantic theme and we chose the French Revolution, with one person, whose identity was kept tightly secret, nominated by our Committee to be the Scarlet Pimpernel; and a prize offered for his or her identification before midnight.

The evening included champagne and canapés, a three course dinner, with wine, speeches, an auction of promises, dancing, casino and ice bar and clues to the Pimpernel. The auction, run brilliantly by Hugo Swire, later MP for East Devon, included prizes such as a week in a luxury villa in the Algarve, tickets to Wimbledon and to Lords (for the second test against Australia), weekend breaks in selected prestigious country house hotels and other attractive items, all generously donated by friends and families of the Ball Committee.

The Pimpernel's identity was finally revealed to be the Master of Ceremonies, Major Roy Stanger, who was then the Permanent Staff Administrative Officer (PSAO) of the Royal Rifle Volunteers in Milton Keynes and had kindly offered to help us run the evening. His disguise, in his Royal Green Jacket's Mess Kit, was immaculate, but nonetheless, there were, by then, one or two guests hot on his trail!

We were treated, before midnight, to a magnificent fireworks display across the lake down the hill from the Stowe lawns, which run west from the State Rooms, where the dancing took place. The fireworks display ended with a flourish with the letters 'PSP' emblazoned across the sky. Some 272 masked guests came, mainly in exotic dress and it was a memorable and, importantly for the Charity, financially a very successful evening.

Organising the Ball was, however, as those who have successfully run such events know, a tremendous amount of hard work, involving heavy outgoings, high risk and, for the organisers, sleepless nights. Sales of sufficient tickets and a well conducted auction of worthwhile items were the main keys to its success. In the event, we cleared £15,000 and raised considerably the profile of PSP and The PSP Association, particularly in Northamptonshire. As an awareness raiser, it had proved to be as successful as it was as a fundraiser, but at no little cost in terms of the stress, time and effort that went into its planning. As this was mostly by volunteers, their unpaid efforts were much appreciated but their costs were not reflected in the balance sheet. We decided it was definitely worth a repeat, but with an exhausted Ball Committee and Ball Coordinator, to leave it for a year or so and hold the next one in London, being a more attractive venue, we felt, for the majority of the 'younger set'.

Alex Shaw and Jinnie Harman are sisters. They are also two of Sara Koe's first cousins. They organised the three Algarve Rides in Portugal which took place in 2000, 2001 and again in 2007. Alex also became The PSP Association's part time events coordinator for two years in 2000, including for our second Magnolia Ball, held in London in 2001. Both she and Jinnie deserve special mention for their brilliant and efficient support, both playing key roles in these special but labour intensive events.

Their brother Nick Shaw has also supported many of our major events, particularly our New Zealand Club Golf Tournament, and accordingly enters this story later. In March 2000, Jinnie Harman, who lives at Paradiso Alto, near Lagos in Portugal and runs a riding school there, offered to organise, with Rod Frew, a friend of hers and an expert equestrian with great knowledge of the interior of Portugal, a trek on horses, from Alcoutim, on the Spanish border, through the interior of the Algarve, some 300 kilometres (as the crow flies!), following the old Pilgrim's trail through the interior, to Cape St Vincent lighthouse, the most south westerly point in Portugal.

It was proposed to raise funds to be shared equally between The PSP Association and Riding for the Disabled in Portugal. Jinnie had found eight local volunteers there to take part. Rod Frew, who also lives in the Algarve, acted as 'Chief Instructor' and led the ride. It was, we learnt, huge fun though tough going with, on some days, up to ten hours in the saddle. It raised a worthwhile sum and considerable awareness through the local media, for which we were very grateful.

Alex Shaw lives in Silverstone with her partner, John Courtney. She and Jinnie, again with the help of Rod Frew, offered a repeat performance the following year, with more riders. In the event, eight riders from the UK, including Elaine Colton (who was then also working part time for the Association), one from Holland and six from Portugal, led by Rod and Jinnie, arrived at Alcoutim on 7th October 2001. The ride (which was initially planned to take place earlier in the year, but had been delayed to the autumn by an outbreak of foot and mouth disease) then set off.

A support crew, led by Alex and John, followed in transport and, between them, handled the essential back-up administration and the photography. I joined the ride for the last day, having flown out from the UK. Cantering along the sandy beaches just clear of the incoming tide in the sunshine and salty spray toward our final destination was an exhilarating and memorable experience, as was an impressive Portuguese reception at the Lighthouse and party they organised that evening for us afterwards in Lagos, though after five hours in the saddle, I found it difficult to be enthusiastic about dancing, anyway until after some excellent Portuguese wine! Some £5,000 was raised for our Charity alone from this event. It was, however, for the organisers, particularly Jinnie, a staggering amount of work and effort to achieve the memorable success it was for all who took part. With John's photography and some skilful PR, the media in Portugal had a field day and there was good coverage in newspapers and on TV of the event and about PSP and The PSP Association.

On 12th June 2000, we held a Corporate Race Day at Silverstone. Ten teams entered the event, including one led by my son Jamie, through his Company, Redtree LLP. It turned out to be, on the day, mainly a family team, including Jamie's Father-in-Law, Bob Stokes, who had done a bit of car racing in his time, and your Author, who had not, but arrogantly assumed he was just as good as him or anyone else at the wheel!

The day was sunny but very windy and cold. We were all grateful for a warming cup of coffee and a brief by the former Formula One ace, John Watson, at the British Racing Drivers' Club (BRDC) at the start of the day. Our Team advisor was the aptly named 'Welsh wizard', Gethin Jones, a rally specialist. Each team was named after one or another of the Formula 1 racing teams. We chose Jaguar, mainly because the colours were dark green, like those for The PSP Association. We were up against MacLaren, Ferrari, BAR, Arrows, Benetton and Prost. Each Corporate was required to enter a team of ten, to assemble at the Race Course and to compete in five events.

These were

~ **Skid car racing.** Each driver from each team had to complete a timed course around cones, in a Caterham Sports Car, skilfully weight adjusted to make it slide. Times of each member of each team were totalled.

~ **Cross Country Trial.** Each driver from each team had to negotiate a steep muddy track around a circuit in a Range Rover. Skill and time counted.

~ **Driving Skills.** Each driver was taken round the course by an experienced instructor in a Lotus Elise and then asked to complete a lap themselves with their instructor alongside. Marked for skill. Reports read out at the prize giving.

~ **Wheel change.** Each team entered two wheel changing teams. Cars were driven in and wheel changing time recorded.

~ **Formula Racing Car.** The most exciting event! Each driver was given a formula racing car and asked to follow a lead car for two laps, the passenger in which pointed out the markers showing where overtaking was forbidden (disqualification if ignored). Then each team entered two cars in each two lap race. Points were awarded for each successful overtake but deducted for errors. A crash eliminated your team! An unnamed but highly competitive father and son from the Jaguar Team came close to elimination for attempting to overtake each other on a non overtake corner. Penalty points were, however, duly deducted.

More, we suspected, by bribery rather than by outright skill, Jamie's Team, Jaguar, won overall, but with some red faces when the skills reports were read out, including your Author's, "*Michael improved with each lap. Unfortunately there were not enough laps for perfection*"(or anything like it!).

The event finished with a prize giving and dinner at the BRDC. It was a fantastic day enjoyed by all. It was also a good fundraiser, as corporate entries included a worthwhile contribution to the Charity. Like all such events, it required a lot of hard work, coordination and administration, primarily to find and persuade corporates to enter the requisite number of teams prepared to pay their not inconsiderable entry fees and to ensure all teams arrived at the right place, at the right time, with the right number of drivers!

There were the usual concerns of these sort of fun events of having to pay up front and rely on bringing in sufficient 'players' to ensure a better than break-even return. We were nonetheless anxious to do it again, not only for the challenge and fun for those taking part, but for the excellent fundraising returns. Unfortunately for us, Silverstone ceased holding these corporate / charity days the following year, whether, as we suspected, due to the heavy costs of upkeep of the cars we used or abused, or whether because of the expense of the large number of instructional staff involved; or perhaps for some other reason we shall never know!

Of our larger later events, our second Magnolia Ball was held in London. (As mentioned earlier, we were concerned about exhausting the generosity of our Northamptonshire friends). Using a very similar formula to that of our first Ball at Stowe, it took place, courtesy of the Honorary Artillery Company, in the fantastic setting of Armoury House, off City Road on 7th June 2001, in the presence of our Patron, HRH The Duchess of Gloucester, GCVO. It was, coincidently, the day of the General Election, so many guests started off with a visit to their polling booth before preparing for the Ball! We felt it necessary to arrange for a television screen to be placed in an ante room at the Ball for non dancers to keep themselves updated on the election results.

The evening went tremendously well, perhaps despite or perhaps – depending on view point – encouraged by the election results, which were coming in thick and fast at the time and added a certain piquancy to the evening. In any event, all 230 guests appeared really to enjoy themselves. After a champagne reception and speeches, a superb dinner was followed by an auction of promises, carried out with skill and aplomb by Alex Shaw's cousin, the ex-Sotheby's historian Martyn Downer.

There was dancing to a top London Band, a fun casino, a magician and other entertainment, with a raffle drawn at midnight by Lady Naseby, our Chairman's wife. From the Charity's viewpoint, the success of the evening needed to be measured mainly in terms of funds raised, though it was a great awareness raiser and proved to be very helpful in new contacts leading to more funds later. Thanks to the enormous effort made by the Ball Committee, and by Alex Shaw, the Ball Coordinator, we achieved a profit from the evening of £25,500, exceeding our ambitious target. However, it was again hard work for those involved, particularly Committee Members who generously devoted many hours of freely given time persuading generous friends to provide auction items and to 'get up 'tables', etc.

Between Saturday, 26th October and Saturday 2nd November 2002, we organised, with a tour company, a challenging but rewarding sponsored mountain bike ride across the foothills of the Atlas Mountains in Morocco, to raise funds for The PSP Association. The six day event took place in sandy desert and on rocky ridges in temperatures of up to 35 degrees, with the cyclists camping overnight in different locations, guided by an experienced Moroccan called Mustafa, who met our intrepid but by then nervous four volunteers in Marakesh.

Rebecca Benney, then our Events Director, bravely volunteered to be one of those taking part, returning eight days later, browner, fitter and wiser! In her words:

"This had to be one of the most challenging events I've ever let myself in for but, at the same time hugely rewarding. Each day we bicycled some 40kms, yet in the heat and the remote and rough terrain of the high Atlas

Mountains, particularly the high pass onto the plateau of Jebel M'Goun, Morocco's second highest mountain at 4065 metres, it felt like twice that!"

The going was rugged, particularly in the mountains, with frightening drops from goat tracks, up which bicycles had to be pushed or even in places carried. Down hill was more pleasant, but bumpy and exciting. Falls were commonplace. There were many punctures and other repairs necessary. The guide, Mustafa, despite speaking very little English, kept up morale and, during the difficult times, flagging spirits. The support crew included a chef who cooked some amazing meals at campsites, where the support vehicles had arrived earlier to prepare the tents, etc. The campsites themselves were pretty primitive, consisting of basic tents with sleeping bags at night, a mess tent for the day-time stop to shelter from the sun and shower and loo tents. The shower was, in fact, no more than a large plastic bowl of tightly rationed tepid water also to be used for teeth cleaning and washing Aided by a tin mug, the actual shower process itself, was not easy in the dark, despite the brilliantly lit night sky, with its millions of bright emerald stars. All agreed afterwards – if not on some of the more hairy occasions at the time – that it was an amazing experience they would definitely like to do again, given the opportunity.

We considered a repeat the following year, but the overall return on investment was small and it was difficult to attract enough volunteers prepared to pay the underlying costs and add a worth-while contribution to the Charity.

The Reverend Mark Kiddle is an amazingly helpful and resourceful man. He set up, organised and runs a telephone translational service in various languages for emergency services across the UK, as well as undertaking his work in the Church and has built up many useful contacts in the City and at the Guildhall.

He initially contacted us in October 2002 to suggest that we might like to hold a Christmas Carol Service for our Charity at St Clement's East Cheap, a stunningly beautiful small Wren designed Church, two minutes walk from the Bank underground station, off King William Street. It was built soon after the Great Fire had destroyed the earlier building, on land owned by the Church two thousand years ago and survived the London bombing in the Second World War. (The bomb which landed in the nave during a Service failed to explode).

On Thursday 12th December 2002, The PSP Association held its first ever Carol Service at St Clement's. The Reverend Mark Kiddle presided at both this and our subsequent annual Services held there.

We had passed details of this Carol Service to all our contacts in London and, with Mark's help, arranged a Mulled Wine and Mince Pie Reception afterwards the impressive Credit Suisse offices next door at 75 King William Street.

Lessons at this first PSP Association Carol Service were read by our Patron, HRH The Duchess of Gloucester GCVO, Lord Coe KBE (Seb) Sir David Nichols (former Lord Mayor of London), Helen Forster (Dudley Moore's niece), Jeremy Vine, (BBC Newsnight) and Johnny Dankworth (musician and friend of Dudley Moore). The impressive Pegasus Choir sang the twelve carols, six of which were accompanied by the congregation of some 150 supporters.

After the service we walked fifty yards to 75 King William Street to a Reception held in the Queen Victoria Reception Room, courtesy of Credit Suisse, for our mince pies and mulled wine. This, our first Carol Service held in London, would simply not have been possible without the very positive support we were given by the Reverend Mark Kiddle and by the staff of Credit Suisse. The charity received a net sum of nearly £2,000 including that from the collection. Tickets were £20 per head for our first Carol Service.

We decided that this Service should become an annual event, though we would reduce the price of a ticket to £10.

We have held an annual service there, using a similar formula, ever since. Generously supported by the Reverend Mark Kiddle and first by the Pegasus and then the Helios Choir, we return there each year, on the second to last Thursday before Christmas for another memorable Carol Service, well supported by our hierarchy and now firmly on our social calendar.

Each year, Mark kindly kept the money raised by the event in his impressive Church safe overnight. In opening it the next day, after our 2006 service, the key, to his embarrassment, snapped in the lock. It was nearly a month later that an expert safe cracker (reputed to have been 'in the business' in a previous career, but now on the side of the Godly), managed to open it and retrieve our money and Mark's by then much needed Church funds and confidential papers.

On 20th September 2003, we held our third Magnolia Ball back at Stowe. We were fortunate to enjoy a wonderful evening of one of the last real summer days of 2003. Some 220 guests came to the event, to be 'received' by the Royal Green Jackets Buglers and Wind Quartet, courtesy of the then Commanding Officer of the Royal Rifle Volunteers, Lieutenant Colonel Roddy Winser.

There was a Russian theme, with some Cossack dancing. After a champagne reception guests were seated in tables of ten for dinner and Russian songs, sung by Alex Prior, a brilliant young vocalist and by 'Summer', a classical singer, who featured high on the US and UK charts at the time. Following the usual speeches, there was an auction of promises, then dancing to Andy Leek and his band and/or a fun casino. The evening finished at 2 am. It was, again, a huge success, raising some £15,000, but again very hard work to organise and we felt we had perhaps by now exhausted the immensely generous support from friends of the Charity in Northamptonshire.

In the Spring of 2003, we teamed up with the Pegasus Choir for a performance of J.S. Bach's St John Passion, conducted by Jeremy Summerly, well known for his recordings of baroque music. This took place at the spectacular St Luke's Church in Chelsea. The part of the Evangelist was sung by Bene't Coldstream. Members of the Choir and Orchestra were presented after the performance to Our Patron HRH The Duchess of Gloucester GCVO. Some 160 people attended.

On 14th April 2004, we held a special Concert at Leighton House in Holland Park in memory of Dudley Moore, with all proceeds going to support the work of our Association. This concert was the brainchild of Anna Paola, a close personal friend of his, who had often played piano duets with him at his home in London. An impressive line up of performers for the concert included George Melley, with his pianist Ron Rubin, the Actress Eleanor Bron, Clarinettist Tom Whitehouse and the Pegasus Choir. The concert finished with 'Over the Rainbow', one of Dudley's favourite pieces. Wine and soft drinks were served outside. It was a beautiful and memorable evening and an enjoyable and successful event attended by well over a hundred people, including Nigel Dempster, who by then had recently been diagnosed as having PSP.

In October 2004, The PSP Association, courtesy of Nick Shaw (Sara's cousin and Alex's brother), a long time member of the prestigious New Zealand Golf Club, near West Byfleet, and Roger Marrett, the Hon. Secretary (who made up a fourth in one of the teams), held its first Golf Competition there. Despite the dreadful weather forecast, it turned out to be a very pleasant sunny day, with the course in its full autumn glory. Eleven teams entered, including the Lloyds Insurance Brokers Humphrey, Haggis and Sutton, who having called themselves the Ryder Cup Team, had to win. They duly did so, but only following a judgement in their favour by our Appeals Committee, chaired by Nick Shaw, after a shrewd appeal had been lodged by the Cousins' Team!

The day was a great success and it was agreed that this, too, should be an annual event in October and the course booked accordingly. This meant two annual golf competitions run by the Association. We were happy to do so!

Our first Windsor Race Evening took place at the Royal Windsor Racecourse on Monday, 24th July 2006. Even including our Magnolia Balls, this was the most ambitious event we had taken on since the Charity was formed. The broad concept was simple. Charities can buy an evening's racing from the Royal Windsor Race Committee, at the cost of some £24,000 for six races. Covered in this cost is the use of the Riverbank Marquee (though the Charity, of course, pays for the drinks, dinner and service there) and free car park and members' enclosure for up to 200 guests. The 'owner' (purchaser) of each race – and it is up to the charity concerned to find race sponsors – is given free advertising space in race programmes sold to the public attending, an opportunity to feature in the televised race programmes ('Racing Tonight' and 'At the Races'), and also advertising opportunities on the course, plus that accrued in presenting the prize after the race.

The responsibility of the 'bidding' charity is to 'sell' each of its races to corporates and invite up to 300 people to attend.

Our chosen formula was to offer selected corporates a free table of ten at a champagne reception and dinner (we brought in our own champagne and wine, paying corkage, which was, in our view, more cost effective than using the Caterer's supply) in the Marquee, but asking the corporates, in return, to sponsor a race for between £5,000 and £10,000 per race, dependent on its grading.

Lord Coe KBE generously offered to host the reception and dinner, clearly a strong 'pull' for many corporates! Our commitment and down payment had to be early, as these Monday summers' evening races were extremely popular. This early payment by the Charity of substantial outgoings to the Windsor Race Committee put us under considerable pressure to 'perform'; that is to sell some of our races. In doing so, we were wonderfully supported by our Major Fundraising Appeals Committee, made up as described later in this Chapter.

After some sleepless nights as the date approached, we were immensely relieved to have by then firm commitments to purchase four of our six races. The fifth we named the PSP Stakes and the Windsor Race Committee kindly sold on the sixth, as this was to take place during our dinner. At that time, we calculated that we were theoretically 'up' by some £5,000, taking account of the cost of the reception and dinner, so we could breathe more easily.

We planned an 'Auction of Promises' at the end of the dinner and were fortunate that Martyn Downer, the ex-Sotheby's historian, again agreed to be our Auctioneer. We offered additional tables of ten at £900 a table, which gave a small profit on the cost to us of the champagne, two course dinner and wine at the Riverbank Marquee, but also more potential bidders at our auction of promises, on the success of which depended the financial success of the evening.

Windsor is an extremely attractive Race Course skirting the Thames and, with the prospect of a fine evening's racing, our numbers steadily rose. On the day, we had sold just over fifteen tables. It was a glorious summer's evening and thousands of people flooded the racecourse. Our some 150 guests duly arrived and, as the Riverbank Marquee is immediately next to the Parade Ring and racecourse itself, the racing, our reception and the dinner all went down famously. Lord Coe spoke movingly about PSP and afflicted families, before asking Martyn Downer to start the auction. By then, we were running a bit late and with Tuesday being a working day, did not wish to keep our guests up too late, so Martyn was therefore under some time pressure, which he handled with consummate skill and rattled through the items, all of which sold pretty well. Now we could relax after a lovely evening. The Charity ended up with a net profit of some £25,000.

In terms of 'Return on Investment', purist fundraisers would argue that these events are 'marginal' in the sense that, if all goes well, they achieve returns normally of little better than a one-to-one on investment; but involve high risk, with the Charity bearing the cost up front and, if the necessary numbers and sales are not achieved, facing a loss. However, in terms of goodwill, awareness raising and actual outcome, of the nearly thirty events we have run over the years of the Charity's existence, we have only had to 'pull the plug' on two , due to lack of numbers – and even on these we broke even, thanks to generosity of those who had purchased tickets and waived a rebate!. The rest have proved to be highly successful, thanks to a lot of hard work by a large number of people. The view of our Committee at our Windsor 'wash up' was that we should definitely 'do it again' preferably in June 2007, as the end of July was difficult for some with school holidays, etc.

On Sunday, 13th May 2007, we held our third Algarve Ride, using the same formula and organisers as for the first two, including Jinnie, Rod, Alex and John. Twenty experienced riders, all volunteers, from both the Algarve and the UK, assembled that day at Alcoutim on the Guadiana River, which runs along the Spanish/Portuguese border. Each rider had covered their cost of getting there and made a financial contribution toward the event. After a chance for a swim (it was exceptionally hot and dry throughout the ride) everyone met up for dinner and a brief by Rod on the forthcoming event, during which he gave his instructions, with emphasis on safety, particularly on the need to keep in touch with those in front and behind throughout the ride!

Early next morning the riders mounted and set off for their first day in the saddle along the Pilgrim's trail through the forests. For the first few days the weather was kind, but the temperatures steadily rose from a mild 22 to an unseasonable 38 degrees. Sufficient water for both horses and riders became crucial not just for enjoyment but for survival. Tongues of both riders and horses were soon hanging out in the heat of the day! The support crew had to work really hard, undertaking a series of complex logistic manoeuvres. The horse corrals had to be taken down and stored in the lorries along with the buckets, head collars and grooming kit. Suitcases had to be collected, loaded up and ferried either via the mid day rendezvous or direct to the next nights stop, water for horses and re-supply of water bottles for the riders for the mid day break collected and food supplies bought. This alone took three vehicles. The support jeep, where possible, followed the horses, carrying emergency supplies and rider's day packs. Replacements for any rider or horse falling out for any reason also had to be organised.

The ride was not without incident, including a nasty fall involving a badly bruised jaw and some stitches, but no broken bones, and the rider concerned returned for sympathy and the farewell party! All in all, it was a challenging, exciting and memorable event; and riders and horses completing the six days could be proud of their stamina and riding skills. For the final day, temperatures had dropped and, after eight hours in the saddle, to much applause from the assembled crowds, riders and horses finally made it to the lighthouse and were able to touch the wall marking Kilometre Zero or the furthest westernmost point on Mainland Europe.

At the end at the farewell party, there was the odd tear as riders had formed strong bonds with their mounts and with others in the group, during six unforgettable days in the saddle trekking through the breathtakingly beautiful and challenging countryside in an unseasonable Algarve heat wave! Our grateful thanks went to Jinnie, Rod, Alex and John for organising and supervising such a wonderful event for the third time; and the very worthwhile funds it brought in for us. Jinnie was reported to have said, afterwards, "That was fun, but never again!"

On 4th June 2007, we held, as planned, our second Windsor Race Evening, using a very similar formula to the first. One again, Seb generously agreed to host the evening and we set about finding corporates who would sponsor a race. This proved to be a tough assignment and by April, we had only one sponsor, SEI Investments, who had generously taken the main Grade I Race. Then, in the nick of time, in early May, three more sponsors 'volunteered'. An Irish Group, Cannon Kirk, and Scott Wilson, who worked with them 'came in' first, then out of the blue in the nick of time, the Bernard Sunley Foundation generously took our fourth race.

This time we were able to fill over eighteen tables of ten. Once again the weather was kind. After a threatening black cloud had circled Windsor in the morning, the sun came out at midday and it turned into a lovely evening.

The early highlight of the evening was a visit to our Marquee by Frankie Dettori after the Grade I Race, the SEI Stakes, in which he took part (but for once didn't win, but that didn't stop him celebrating with us!).

At the end of a delicious meal, Seb Coe made a moving speech about his Mother and PSP and Martin Pope from ABN AMRO conducted a brilliant fast moving auction. Our feedback was that everyone really enjoyed the evening. The Charity's accounts showed a net profit of £28,000. Both Windsor evenings had involved much hard work by our MFAC (one of its members was Andrew Tusa, who is also a Trustee of The PSP Association. His son is a good friend of Frankie Dettori's daughter, hence Frankie's visit to our Marquee after the race) and by our own team organising the detail. Once again, Hugo Bevan, who had been Clerk of the Course both at Windsor and Towcester, proved an invaluable coordinator between us and the Race Course. Our third race evening, compered by Jane Hardy on 4th July 2008 with, once again, Seb, as our host, was another huge success, with over twenty tables of ten coming on the day. Hence we are planning a fourth go in 2009!

Fundraising events organised by others, in which we took part

The Flora London Marathon had, by 1999, already become one of the Charity's main fundraising events and, over the next eight years, we planned to increase the number of people running for us and the revenue the event brought in. To do this, we needed to acquire more 'Golden Bonds'.

We were fortunate that the London Marathon had then yet to achieve the enormous popularity it now has; and we were able, over the next couple of years, to purchase, on behalf of the Association, a 'book' of over fifty renewable Golden Bonds.

For those who have not been involved in the administration of London Marathon, a Golden Bond guarantees an entry for a 'would be' runner. For example, if you apply through the ballot and are turned down, you can then approach any charity with spare Golden Bonds and negotiate a deal in which the charity offers you a guaranteed place in return for your commitment to raise a specified amount of money for the charity.

At that time, a limited number of Golden Bonds could be purchased ahead by a charity from the London Marathon Organisers, on a five year renewable basis (when last available) at £250 plus VAT per Bond per year. As all spaces for the Marathon are now already allocated – either through the ballot or through Golden Bonds already bought by charities – additional Bonds can only be acquired following a charity opting out of renewal and handing back/over some of their allocation or through the Organisers taking in still more runners, enabling them to offer further Bonds - neither of these being today a likely or regular occurrence.

Golden Bonds are consequently in great demand, particularly for those runners unlucky in the ballot but still keen to run. Charities advertise the availability of their purchased Golden Bond

1. *HRH The Duchess of Gloucester, GCVO*

2. *The Lord Bramall, KG, GCB, OBE, MC*

3. *The Lord Guthrie of Craigiebank GCB, LVO, OBE*

1. The Lord Coe KBE

2. Professor Colin Blakemore

3. Tim Boswell MP

4. David McDonough OBE

5. Nigel Jones, Solicitor

1. *Lord Naseby PC*

2. *Sir Michael Carleton-Smith CBE*

3. *Sir John Greenaway Bt*

4. *Elizabeth Kennedy*

5. *Brian Pascoe*

6. *Bryan Fisher*

1. *James Stanford*

2. *Andrew Fenwick*

3. *Andrew Tusa*

4. *Christopher Kemball*

5. *Simon Koe*

6. *James Koe*

1. *Richard Kirby*

2. *Peter Glithero*

3. *Joanna Tomkinson*

4. *Nigel Down*

5. *Holly Bellingham*

6. *Lady Turner (Deborah)*

1. *Jane Hardy*

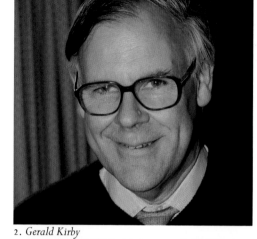

2. *Gerald Kirby*

3. *Alex Wyman*

4. *Katie Hodges (left)*

5. *Sarah Wollaston*

6. *Peter Cover*

1. *Rebecca Benney*

2. *John Chandler*

3. *Debra Chand*

4. *Marilyn Osbourne*

5. *Dr Angela Wilson*

6. *Nigel Slater*

1. *Maggie Rose*

2. *Tess Astbury*

3. *Grace Lewis*

4. *Cathy Magee*

5. *Jill Lyons*

6. *Samantha Pavey*

1. Caroline Clews

2. Debbie Benadie

3. Tricia Holmes

4. Maureen Fowler

5. Gina Rutterford

6. Sandra Campbell

7. Kathy Miller-Hunt

8. Michael Scott

9. Madeleine Quine

1. *Nichola Brookman*

2. *Jaine Colwell*

4. *Bernie Herriot*

5. *Cameron Wood*

3. *Sarah O'Connor*

6. *Cliff Davies*

7. *Alan Berry*

8. *Lorraine Bowers*

9. *Lis Nunn*

10. *Jean Atkins*

11. *Elaine Elcoat*

12. *Lesley Wood*

13. *Sharron Arrowsmith*

1. *Professor Andrew Lees*

2. *Professor Lawence Golbe*

3. *Professor Martin Rossor*

4. *Professor John Hardy*

5. *Professor Werner Poewe*

6. *Professor Yves Agid*

1. *Professor John Steele*

2. *Professor Eduardo Tolosa*

3. *Professor Irene Litvan*

4. *Professor Niall Quinn*

5. *Professor Nick Wood*

6. *Dr Philippe Damier*

1. *Professor John Hodges*

2. *Professor David Burn*

3. *Professor Tamas Revesz*

4. *Professor Gavin Giovannini*

5. *Professor Nigel Leigh*

6. *Dr Luke Massey*

1. *Dr Peter Pramstaller*

2. *Dr Thomas Bak*

3. *Dr Uma Nath*

4. *Dr Dominic Paviour*

5. *Dr Rohan de Silva*

6. *Dr Huw Morris*

1. Dr Anette Schrag

2. Dr Diane Hanger

3. Dr Richard Wade-Martins

4. Dr Pau Pastor

5. Dr Adam Zermansky

6. Dr David Williams

1. Dr Margaret Piggott

2. Dr Selina Wray

3. Dr Naomi Warren

4. Susan Stoneham

5. Linda Parsons

6. Connie Luk

7. Kate Strand

places in various runners' magazines, such as those now put out by the Flora London Marathon Organisers. People who wish to run in this event are asked therein to apply for a place through the advertising charity. This involves the runner committing to raise the minimum of between £800 and £2,000, now asked by most Golden Bond owning charities. We kept to the lower end of this scale, but encouraged our runners to raise more. Meanwhile, we continued to pester Dave Bedford, the then Chief Executive of the London Marathon Organisation, for any handed back Golden Bonds we could purchase from them.

The number of our Bonds grew steadily from ten in 1996, rising to over fifty after our successful purchase of our first large tranche. By the summer of 2007, adding together our 'Golden Bond' runners and those successful in the ballot, we had built up to very close to 100 people running for The PSP Association in the annual Flora London Marathon. (In 2007, for example, we had 103 runners two weeks before the event, but with last minute drop outs due to injuries, a tantalising 99 on the day, our highest number yet of actual runners in this event). The funds raised by sponsorship, taking account of costs, built up rapidly from £10,000 in 1995 to approaching £100,000 in 2007, which made this event the largest single fundraiser in our calendar year.

Although most of our runners have been organised, capable and efficient, needing little if any backup, all require timely information together with some support. Inevitably a few require considerable 'spoon feeding' and/or bailing out! Some ten to fifteen each year fall by the wayside, as the race approaches, through injury or another unforeseen event.

Our traditional pasta party in Notting Hill (which we offer our runners the evening before so that they can meet up with others running for us before the race), our support of the event itself and our 'after marathon care', taken together, mean we increasingly rely on our runners raising more than their minimum commitment to reach our target in sponsorship money. For the cost of purchasing and advertising the Golden Bonds themselves, the increasing cost of administering runners and other overheads also all add up. It would be fair to say that the great majority, in fact, raise much more than the minimum amount.

Our 'after marathon care' relies largely on the generosity of the Association of British Pharmaceutical Industry (ABPI), who through the good offices of Marjorie Johnson, loan us rooms in their strategically placed building overlooking Trafalgar Square. We have been able to meet our exhausted runners there, offer them a relaxing shower, a massage or 'running repairs' and something to eat with their families after they have completed the event. The view from the ABPI top floor windows is uplifting for them, too!

Human nature being what it is, there are, inevitably, a handful of runners who fail to honour their commitment to send in any or all of the funds they had agreed to raise for us. Where we judge the runner has made little or no effort to do so, we pass their names on to the London Marathon Organisers to add to their 'non performers' list. However, the vast majority go to extraordinary lengths, having taken one of our Golden Bond places, to bring in sums way above their target and many companies are generous in matching funds raised by those working for them.

We have now had over a thousand PSP sponsored runners taking part in this one event, and this number includes a growing and heart warming group of researchers working in the PSP field, who have volunteered to run to raise funds for us. Dr Andrew Evans, an Australian Doctor attached for a six month sabbatical to Professor Andrew Lees' team, completed the London Marathon in 2 hours 33 minutes, and, we believe, holds the current PSP Association record for this event.

Dr Dominic Paviour, who undertook the Serial MRI Scanning Research, was a Sara Koe Research Fellow. He, in the tradition of our younger Research Fellows, ran for us in the New York Marathon, completing with his brother Ben, who achieved a time of 2 hours 39 minutes. Dominic came in a few minutes later!

The current record for a PSP runner in any Marathon was, however, actually achieved in the same race by Shane Snow, who completed the event in 2 hours 23 minutes, being the second fastest British runner to finish that day.

Other of our runners have also competed in a variety of different marathons around the world, though the New York Marathon has been perhaps the most popular. On 7th November 1997, my four sons and twelve of their friends ran in this exciting and immensely well run and supported event and by 1998, the number of PSP runners flying to New York for the Marathon had built up to 52. The following three years on the first Sunday in November The PSP Association entered some forty runners per year. In 2001, a few months after the terrorist attack on, and devastation of, the Twin Towers, we entered our last New York Marathon before the rules changed. It was beautiful late autumn, or 'fall', weather and New Yorkers were just beginning to recover from this devastating blow, but the scars were still very visible. The site itself was closed off by boarding, on which were posted thousands of moving notes by relatives and friends of those who had died in this horrific terrorist attack.

The rules for the New York Marathon changed from 2002 and, for us, it thereby became very much more difficult and expensive. Charities could no longer purchase entries direct from the New York Marathon Runners Club. Two UK Tour Operators were given control of entries from the UK to this event and charged £950 per head for flight and entry, whereas previously Charities had paid only for an entry – some £50 – plus the cost of a flight, which was around £200.

Entries too had to be firmly booked with the Tour Operators and paid for up front – up to eight months in advance! 'Flight and entry only' also became harder to obtain because, from the Tour Operators viewpoint, a package of flight, entry and hotel was a much more lucrative deal for them and therefore was given greater priority. We continued to encourage entries for this challenging and unique event, wonderfully supported by New Yorkers, but costs per head and money up front put off many British runners, so numbers dropped sharply accordingly. We branched out into other easier to enter Marathons, like Edinburgh, Dublin, Paris and Berlin, but continued to encourage those runners who could afford it, to give New York, a fabulous event, a go.

The Marathon des Sables is billed as the toughest footrace in the world. It takes place annually in Morocco. In the Spring of 2003, my son Richard and two of his friends, Barnes Martin and William Eaglestone, entered this formidable event as a team to raise funds for our Charity.

The start is about 2 hours drive across the Sahara from Ouarzazate. Each team sets out carrying all their supplies for six days, including food, compasses, clothing, cameras, sleeping bags etc plus 20 litres of water – further water is supplied at check points The going included sand dunes and open desert in temperatures up to 50°c in the day plummeting to near freezing at night. There are six stages. One leg alone is over 80 kilometres. Our team completed the six stages over seven days in a total running time of 61 hours 42 minutes. They raised from this one event just over £51,000 for the Charity, with some very generous donors, matched by Richard's then boss, Dr Spiro Latsis.

Richard takes up the story below:

"Imagine leaving the supermarket carrying the weekend's shopping. It's a hot midsummer's day and you're wearing a raincoat, a woolly hat, and badly fitting Wellington boots, without socks. Go to a ploughed field and carry the shopping – at a shuffle, from one side of the field to the other. Carry on doing that for at least nine hours. Then you can sleep on the earth, treat your blisters and eat some powdered meals. Continue doing the same for 7 days.

As I dragged myself across the Sahara, this was the best analogy I could think of to the immense challenge of the Marathon des Sables. Of course, no English summer's day I can remember has got close to the 50 degrees we baked in, and I have not mentioned that one leg of this torturous race was over 80km. That day-night-day's journey took 29 hours, and included a 3 hour stop whilst Barnes was put on an intravenous drip. During that surreal night the sky's myriad of stars was intermittently lit up with flares, set off by competitors who could no longer continue. We passed one such runner who had been bitten by a scorpion.

Over 7 days we completed all 6 legs of the Marathon, and finally, and with ecstatic relief, crossed the finishing line early Saturday afternoon. That day the temperature had passed 45 degrees by 10am. Many of us had carried worsening blisters for several days, most of us had various forms of stomach cramp from the incessant and monotonous consumption of glucose and isotonic drinks and gels, and none of us had changed clothes or washed in a week. But we'd eaten half the weight off our rucksacks, and could smell the finish (no doubt it could also smell us!).

At last, I felt I could run rather than stumble the last 25 km. As I stepped onto the tarmac – the first road I'd seen in a week – and saw the finish line ahead, I grabbed out the PSP flag I'd packed and used as a pillow through the race. I held it out and slowed to march it across the finish line. And when our team regrouped a few minutes later, all successful finishers, we flew the flag for a final photograph. Already, as I write, I am far removed from that scorching oven of rubble rock and powdery brown sand. But that moment of triumph is indelible, and I will always be incredibly proud that our team took The PSP Association's colours from start to finish of the Marathon des Sables."

Other events in which our subscribers and friends have taken part include challenges like the

Three Peaks, which involves climbing Ben Nevis, Scaffell Pike and Snowdon, in a 24 hour period – a tough call – and the Thames Meander, a 54 km run starting at Reading and following the Thames to London, usually undertaken by runners as a precursor to the Marathon des Sables. My youngest son Digby, not to be seriously outrun by his elder brother, completed the Thames Meander in February 2005 in 11 hours, 8 minutes, coming 33rd out of 101 competitors, some twenty of whom dropped out. He almost joined the drop outs, when a small error in map reading took him, as dusk fell, into a cul de sac on the outskirts of London, where a terrified elderly lady thought he was about to attack her, when he chased after her to ask her the way out of what by then seemed, in his disorientated state of mind, an endless maze from which he would never exit.

In 2006, The Association entered a team in an Arctic Dog Sledding Challenge in Sweden. The Challenge offered participants the chance to learn the basic skills of 'mushing' whilst taking responsibility for their own team of huskies. Over a week, they worked closely with the dogs, adapting their life styles to one of the harshest environments on earth, whilst learning new skills. Minimum sponsorship was £3,000, so it was not cheap! We received a fascinating report from them of their adventure. Because this event was organised by a specialist company, there was little administration involved for the charity and a worthwhile return. We would hope to provide a full team next time we take this on!

Rob Swerling is a good friend of my son Richard. They were at Oxford together. Rob, having already run in a Marathon for the Association, offered, in 2005, to hold a quiz evening at Bush House in London for some twenty tables of six to raise funds for the Charity. The questions were tough and only a few highly intelligent and knowledgeable tables with remarkable recall of current affairs and celebrity affairs scored more then fifty percent. Our table managed ten percent and we were far from last! It was, however, a fun evening and raised a sufficiently worthwhile sum for a repeat in 2006. Sandra Campbell, our Development Officer in Northern Ireland, held a similar event in Belfast and raised £1,270 from some extremely generous guests.

Fundraising appeals and the general public

There is today intense competition for the public's attention, with more and more 'begging letters' from an ever increasing number of good causes. Charities seeking to fundraise from the general public are finding there is increasingly tough competition to do so. The public are much wiser than they are often given credit for and will usually quietly assess needs in light of their own experience, knowledge of the cause and personal preferences in responding to the rapidly growing number of appeals coming through their letter boxes.

Factors affecting their response, however, include awareness and 'pull'. Someone who knows about PSP and its symptoms or has an even more direct experience, with a family member having suffered from the disease, is much more likely to respond positively. People prioritise their support, as they continue to be bombarded with an increasing range of ever more emotive appeals.

Those appeals on behalf of children and other worthy good causes such as disaster relief around the world are rightly likely to be given priority over neurodegenerative diseases such as PSP and support for the elderly (though as we age ourselves, there is some temptation to redirect priorities!). Prevalence and nastiness are factors taken into account. Cancer and Alzheimer's for example will attract a worthwhile share of giving in the health field. Lesser known and rarer diseases, however devastating, will always struggle to compete, even proportionately. The greater the awareness, the more successful the appeal is a self evident conclusion.

In 1997, we were given our first slot by BBC Radio 4's 'This Week's Good Cause'. Sebastian Coe – as he then was – generously agreed to make the Appeal. The results were particularly pleasing for the Charity, bringing in both raised awareness and some £10,000 in donations. Sending thank you letters to all donors and keeping records of their details stretched our resources at the time (all our team gathered around the table each to write their share) but paid dividends in later appeals. We were careful to remove from our lists those few who said enough was enough! Under the BBC's 'waiting' rule, we had to wait at least four years to apply again.

On 27th May 2001, the BBC gave us our second 'go' on this programme. Its name by then had changed to BBC Radio 4 Appeal. This time Gemma Craven, the actress, whose father Gabriel had died from PSP, spoke movingly about the disease and its effect on her family. A total of a little over £12,000 was raised this time.

Our third appeal was broadcast on 26th November 2006 – again by Lord Coe. Although the amount brought in by the appeal was less that we had optimistically hoped, this was not really surprising, as it immediately followed a children's appeal; and there had been the previous day some quite hostile press about the cost of the Olympic Games. One listener wrote:

"Dear Seb,

Why don't you just cut back a few hundred thousand pounds on the 2012 Olympics and give it to The PSP Association!"

Unfortunately, life is not that simple. We were very grateful to Lord Coe for taking this on again and well pleased with what came in and the welcome lift in awareness that his excellent broadcast brought us.

Early on, we established an annual appeal to our Subscribers around Magnolia Day. This initially took the form of a raffle, based on some very generous and attractive items donated by friends of the Charity. This involved quite a lot of administration, but brought in over £2000 each year. Nigel Slater as our Fundraising Consultant introduced, in 2006, our first NewsExtra, another successful appeal, outlined below.

Fundraising from Donor Trusts and Corporates

Over a third of the Charity's income has come to date from Donor Trusts, many of whom Sarah Wollaston, our young and impressive Director of Fundraising, researched from reference books and our IT library. We worked on the basis that, having looked at our commitments, we selected projects of possible interest to them. Having learnt as much as possible about the trusts we planned to target, we would agree, for each selected Donor Trust, a Project within their area of interest and Sarah would have a first go at a draft to them, seeking funding for our selected Project.

This system involved a great deal of painstaking work in matching Project to interest, costing it and applying accordingly, having judged the likely financial support on offer. For example, a piece of cutting edge research that our Charity had already agreed to sponsor over, say, three years, might, we felt, be of particular interest to, say, 'The Henry Smith Charity'. So we would then put on paper details of the proposed research and of the help we needed from them toward it. Sarah became highly skilled in putting these applications together and in her approach; and our 'hit rate' became impressively high.

We were deeply shocked in the autumn of 2005 to learn from Sarah that she had been diagnosed as having an aggressive form of Multiple Sclerosis (MS), another devastating neurodegenerative disease. Sarah has two young children. She was now facing, with enormous courage, the implications for herself and her family of this disease and its progression. She was keen to continue work, but by early 2006, she was effectively wheelchair bound, although she could still come to the office once a week. Nigel Slater, a friend who lived locally and had recently retired as Fundraising Director of the Leprosy Mission, agreed to support us as a part time fundraising consultant to help out Sarah as long as she could continue.

In this role, he introduced and coordinated the production of 'NewsExtra', a fundraising newsletter which we put out on a wide circulation (some 5,000 copies) in April 2006 around our Magnolia Day. This first issue was well received by the Association's many friends and supporters and raised over £10,000, net of printing and postage. Our second NewsExtra went out a year later and was equally successful. It, once again, involved a great deal of hard work and time.

By early 2007, Sarah was wheelchair bound, but still determined to carry on work fundraising for us. She was, however, only able to visit Wappenham once a fortnight, driven by her husband or a carer. She felt she could continue to handle Donor Trust applications, but could no longer act as a Director, coordinating the charity's overall fundraising.

We, therefore, reluctantly agreed to advertise for a new Director for whom Sarah would work. Once again, we were lucky to find someone with the purpose, skill and energy to take our fundraising forward. Marilyn Osborne had worked for six years with the Royal National Institute for Deaf People (RNID); and with Sarah's support, very quickly integrated with our team, bringing in fresh initiatives. Once she was settled in, Nigel left us, as planned, to pursue other avenues. We were very grateful for his hard work, experience and advice, during his time as our fundraising consultant.

Since starting this book, I have learnt that, sadly, Sarah has had to cease to work for us, as her focus has had to be more and more on her family and her MS, as the disease progresses.

Former Olympic Gold Medallist, Lord Coe (Seb) had been President of our Marathon Committee for over seven years, when he learnt in May 2003 that his Mother, Angela had PSP. This was a tough blow for his family and we empathised with their resulting concerns as her condition deteriorated. Seb was determined to do all he could for her; and to give us his full support in our fundraising and awareness efforts. Good as his word, he visited our Offices on 13th October 2003, and during the visit, agreed to Chair The PSP Association Major Fundraising Appeals Committee (MFAC) that Sarah Wollaston and I had discussed several times.

We invited other influential members. Peter Fenwick, a good friend of The Charity and uncle of Andrew Fenwick, one of our Trustees, offered to advise us on how it should operate. Other members included Nigel Down, a Director of SEI Investments, a Trustee of the Charity and family friend, Christopher Kemball (who had served with the author as a Royal Green Jacket), a Director of Hawkpoint, an influential City Firm, another good and influential friend, (who also later became a Trustee), the very supportive Ian Barclay, whose Wife, Elizabeth sadly died from PSP in 2005, after a brave fight, Nicholas Archer, in PR (who later had to resign because of changing jobs and pressure of work), and Andrew Tusa, (whose Mother had recently died of PSP and whose sister, Helen Barkshire, had written the soft food cookery book). Andrew was then a Director of Deutsche Asset Management and is now with Merrill Lynch. The first Meeting of our MFAC duly took place at the House of Lords, chaired by Lord Coe, on 5th February 2004, when we set ourselves an ambitious target of raising one million pounds.

Over the next three years, we held some six Meetings a year to develop and build on our initial design. The plan we used involved each member listing all their contacts with people, such as Trustees of Charitable Trusts, Foundations and Livery Companies, thereby seeking to 'open doors' for The PSP Association to people in a position financially to help the Charity. The aim was to enable The PSP Association to meet such contacts and present about the Charity's work and its need for support.

This usually involved my visiting, often with the MFAC Member concerned, the contact and giving them a PowerPoint laptop presentation on our work. If they were interested, Sarah Wollaston would then put together a written appeal, within their area of interest, for a Project, perhaps on support for afflicted families or perhaps for a piece of cutting edge research. This networking approach produced impressive results. Our MFAC also held a dinner in the House of Lords for influential friends, who could – and mainly did – help us in raising further funds.

They also became involved in other important fundraising areas, including helping us develop partnerships with major corporates, such as WS Atkins, the Engineering giant, (through Christopher Kemball), Scottish & Southern Electricity, (through Andrew Tusa), and MarketForm at Lloyds and Integro, (through my son Simon), all of whom have helped us either financially or in other different but important-to-us ways; Holly Bellingham, Chair of MarketForm, a Medical Underwriter, has not only generously sponsored some of our work, but also became a Trustee of the Charity.

We have also been supported most generously by a wide range of Donor Trusts, many of whom have made extremely welcome donations toward our work, toward the remuneration of our staff and toward the research we sponsor. These donors are meticulously thanked in The PSP Association's newsletters and of course directly. It would, however, be invidious here in this book to mention just some; and there is simply not room enough for all who have given toward our cause to be included here. Their individual and collective contributions, however, have been absolutely vital to our success and the support we have been able to provide PSP patients and Carers, as well as research into the cause, effective treatment and eventual cure of this devastating disease. My successor, Jane Hardy, keeps in close touch with many of these and their continuing support is enormously important to us.

Our MFAC, in addition to its 'introductory' work, has helped us in many other ways, such as its direct involvement and support for our Windsor Race Evenings, which Seb has generously hosted over the last three years, and over our crucial-to-us appeal to the prestigious October Club.

Peter Fenwick's nephew, Andrew, was by then the Financial Director of Brunswick PR, suggested we applied for funding from the prestigious October Club. Once a year, since 1988, this philanthropic London based asset management Committee organise a fundraising dinner at the Savoy for over 400 of the City of London's most influential people to raise a substantial transformational sum for their selected Charity of the Year. Their aim, expressed by their then Chairman, David McDonough, is simple: "to raise significant funds for small and remarkable charities in order to transform their fortunes".

We applied accordingly, but were rejected in 2003, when the October Club selected a wonderful Charity, The TreeHouse Trust, who sought to tackle the woeful lack of appropriate services across the UK for children with autism. We tried again in 2004. This time we were initially placed on a short list and invited to make a presentation to Members of the October Club in London. Sarah and I put together a PowerPoint presentation to some fifteen members of the Club. There were one or two technical hitches and I didn't feel I put over our story or answered their probing questions as well as I would have liked. In the taxi back to Euston afterwards, I apologised to Sarah. I felt I had 'blown' a wonderful opportunity and waited the next day for confirmation that we had been rejected. David McDonough, however, much to my surprise, rang promptly the next morning to give me the wonderful news that the Committee had unanimously selected us as their Charity of the year for 2004. We were over the moon!

For the next few months, the Charity was kept extemely busy in helping organise the evening. The October Club Committee were very experienced and have amazing contacts – and we were prepared 'to work our socks off' for such a fantastic opportunity, not only to raise substantial funds but to spread awareness amongst an audience charities would move mountains to address. As the year went by, excitement grew within The PSP Association.

At last that October evening at the Savoy arrived. Before the auction of promises, David Mac-Donough spoke:-

"A warm welcome to our seventeenth dinner. This year we are tackling a shocking and little known disease: Progressive Supranuclear Palsy. It's as common as Motor Neurone Disease but enjoys only a fraction of MND's popular recognition. In the UK alone, it has 10,000 victims, including Nigel Dempster. It killed Dudley Moore and consequently took off as a charity in the States. But not here in the UK.

Here, the PSP Association only came into existence ten years ago, formed by a retired Brigadier, Michael Koe, whose wife suffered and died from PSP. Michael and a tiny staff have been running the charity - and its help lines for the families of sufferers - from outbuildings in his house in Towcester. They have raised enough money to be both an information provider and to fund some key research - a fantastic achievement.

The Committee embraced this brave and splendid charity without one dissenting voice. We all saw the chance to transform their fortunes. Our aim tonight is to shoot for £400,000 - half will go to setting them up in proper offices run by a new Chief Executive (Michael Koe is retiring from the role but will stay very active) and small staff; and the other £200,000 will go into cutting edge research at University College Hospital under the direction of Professor Andrew Lees. His research programme is all about finding ways of reducing the more ghastly physical effects of PSP's remorseless and deadly advance.

I hope you agree that the PSP Association is a perfect October Club beneficiary in every way, giving us the chance to be truly transformational. It is worthy of your whole hearted support tonight.

My thanks go to this year's committee; to my hardworking and successful working' Group; to the Ascot Race Day Committee and particularly Paul Roy and NewSmith Capital Partners for generously sponsoring our successful Race Day; to the wonderful and indispensable Michele Hunter and to Janis Moore, Virginia Halewood and Deborah Staines for all their help.

Have a great evening - and please make it one to remember for the PSP Association."

Thanks to the enormous generosity of the October Club and all attending the dinner, a truly amazing figure of over £400,000 was raised for The PSP Association that evening. We had previously agreed the division of funds raised with David MacDonough and his Committee. At that time, a new and larger office was high on our list, having finally outgrown the outbuildings of my house. In the event, our new offices were largely paid for by an unexpected legacy; and the October Club's funds went into research and core costs (mainly more staff) to help meet our rapid growth in both commitment and size.

Gift aid, tax efficient giving and interest on capital and shares

Since the Charity was formed, every opportunity has been taken to emphasise the benefits of Tax Efficient Giving. In the early years, Deeds of Covenant were the principal way in which charities could reclaim tax on donations, but the rules governing such covenants were quite restrictive and the take-up was small. With effect from April 2000, however, major changes were introduced and the current system of Gift Aid came into effect. This removed all the inflexibility associated with Covenants and imposed a very simple regime. Any donation could qualify as long as the donor was a UK tax-payer (income or capital gains tax) and, in the year in which the donation in question was made, paid an amount of such tax at least equivalent to the amount reclaimable by the charity (currently 28p in the pound). In other words, for a donation of £100, the charity can reclaim £28 as long as the donor has paid at least this amount in qualifying taxes during the tax year in which the donation was made. Thus some of the massive contribution from the October Club was eligible for tax relief, further enlarging their generous donations.

In the 2008 Budget, it was announced that charities would be able to continue claiming repayment at 28% for a further three years, not withstanding the fact that the basic rate of income tax would change to 20% with effect from 6th April 2008, which would have effectively reduced the reclaim percentage to 25%. Had this concession not been made, it has been estimated that charities collectively would have lost approximately £90 million per annum.

For The PSP Association, Gift Aid has proved to be a very valuable additional income stream. In FY 2006/07 (the last full year for which figures are available), some £29,000 was reclaimed and in the current year, it is hoped to exceed this figure.

There are other forms of Tax Efficient Giving, notably Payroll Giving and the gifting of securities. Neither of these has had a major impact on The PSP Association, although an anonymous benefactor did gift two holdings of ordinary shares in 2001 - one in Rio Tinto Zinc, which over time has proved to be a remarkably successful investment and asset.

As the Charity grew, we were able to invest funds in interest bearing accounts, which ensured a reserve for 'a rainy day' and provides income from interest to help with core costs. As, in turn, these investments grew, our Financial Policy Committee, described in Chapter 3, advised Trustees on a balanced low risk investment strategy to bring in optimum returns. Chapter 8 accordingly returns to the financial scene.

8. *Charity finances*

The PSP Association effectively opened its financial books when Trustees, at our first Executive Committee Meeting, generously agreed that each would put £25 into the kitty, to help us 'get going' soon after the Charity was registered. For the first two years, financial control was comparatively simple. John Greenaway and I were able to keep 'on top' and plan ahead using 'Money Manager' software to control income and expenditure and enable the Charity to be transparent and comply with Charity Law and Companies Acts.

Dr Pramstaller became our first research fellow in 1996, with us sponsoring a just affordable six months of his basic salary, so that he could undertake his Project for the Charity. Before that, our main outgoings had revolved around our Telephone Counselling Service, our Local Support Groups, our IT, our website and our other core costs. Charity income was, however, growing fast by then and drawing up and implementing our first business plan and annual budget was to keep us focussed and 'on the ball' for the next year.

Charity budgets (and, of course, business plans) are drawn up in many different ways, but the same basic principles apply. For the first two years, following registration, John Greenaway and I used essentially a combination of two different routes to draw up our early budgets for Trustees' approval for the following year, involving:-

~ assessing cash expenditure – looking at our priority aims for the year within each objective and costing them; then adding up the total expenditure needed per objective and overall,

~ estimating cash income – assessing how much money might reasonably be raised from different sources available to us, then allocating a share toward each objective. The 'share out' we applied, after setting aside a sum for 'minimum reserves' (see below), was broadly 35% for research, 30% for awareness (including 'seed corn' fundraising), 30% for support and 5% for core costs, including administration.

We then matched the two, re-examining both routes to achieve a balance. This was a comparatively straightforward process. As the Charity grew, we changed our financial year to run from 1st July to 30th June rather than more normal 1st April to 31st March to fit in with our biannual Trustees' Meetings, despite the additional complication of aligning our figures to those produced using the financial year of related organisations, such as the Department of Health.

Thereafter, each year saw, in March, the start of our next year's budget planning. When John departed to attend to farming and family business, Gerald Kirby took over the financial reins of the Association, as mentioned in Chapter 3. Gerald lived in nearby Weston, the next village to John in Weedon Lois. His career had been in banking, at Baring's, so he was able to bring timely financial skills and expertise, as the Charity's income and outgoings grew and budgeting ahead became daily more complicated.

He and I, as respectively Financial Controller and Chief Executive, would put together, based on our 'in-house' Business Plan, a first draft budget, which we then developed with Peter Glithero, our Treasurer, for final approval at our Trustees Meeting in June, for implementation over our next financial year. We took as a 'starter' the Business Plan figure for budgeted income available for the year (the total of the previous year's income, plus seven percent, plus if required, any 'available reserves'; that is, any amount left in reserve over and above the minimum laid down by Trustees.

These minimum reserves were set so that the Charity could, if necessary, meet at least half of the following year's expenses, excluding any income brought in. Thus, should income totally dry up, there would be enough to cover the first six months of the year ahead. (From 2007, with further growth of the Charity, this mandatory reserve was reduced by Trustees from six to four months, to be consistent with similarly medium sized Charities).

Gerald and I would next cost, for the financial year under consideration, the research to which the Charity was already committed, and add any further new research that we expected Trustees to approve at the following June and November Meetings; and compare the cost of this total with research income (the thirty five percent) we had provisionally allocated.

If, as usual, the former was higher, we inclined, if the research was cutting edge and well Peer Reviewed, just to add its cost to the research income forecast, on the basis that Donor Trusts were more likely to be generous, if we could appeal to them to support an interesting piece of research, rather than just asking them to fund some of the Charity's more routine information and support or awareness engendering projects. In other words, we would just increase the amount we would budget to raise for research from Donor Trusts to meet the increase.

Following the Association of Medical Research Charities guidelines, we aimed to take on Research Fellows offering a two or three year Research Project into PSP (which at least two independent Peer Reviewers considered sufficiently relevant and high grade), focussing on a key area identified by our Medical Advisory Panel and by our International Medical Workshops. By sponsoring the Research Fellow rather than consumables and other aspects of the research proposed, we sought a longer term return consequential to the interest in PSP developed by the Research Fellow.

Estimating annual Research spending was not easy. Say our selected Research Fellow was carrying out Trustee approved and sponsored work for the Charity over a three year period, starting on the 1st January of the year in question. His or her basic salary would be paid by the University concerned and invoiced quarterly in arrears to the Charity – often up to a couple of months late. At that stage, our budgets were based on actual income and outgoings – not accrued. Hence, reconciling actual likely outgoing for a piece of research over the Charity's financial year, demanded some quite complex guess estimates, together with some adjustments to allow for the actual, as opposed to planned, start of work stated in the researcher's application (as well as in likely delays from the Universities in invoicing us for monies due to, and payable by, the Charity). Forecast annual research expenditure over a four year period from the previous year to three years ahead was calculated accordingly and presented at biennial June and November Meetings in the form of a Research Expenditure Table, showing estimated figures both including and excluding proposed research, to be taken at that Meeting.

Our aim was to take on as much cutting edge research as we safely could and to seek to convince our Treasurer and Trustees that the risks in so doing were acceptable, bearing in mind that we were likely to benefit from Donor Trust support for such research. It always made for an interesting balancing act.

This balancing was further complicated by a commitment Trustees made when the Sara Koe PSP Research Centre (SKRC) was established in London in 2002. This commitment was for an annual grant from The PSP Association to the SKRC, initially for £100,000 a year, toward the cost of the Centre. This grant would be indexed to inflation. It would be paid each financial year, quarterly in arrears, to the SKRC through University Colleges, London (UCL), who would invoice the Association accordingly.

Trustees amended the size of this grant at a Meeting in 2004 to a figure to match the basic salaries of an Administrator (Ms Susan Stoneham), a Research Technician (Mrs Linda Parsons, nee Kilford), and a Research Fellow (currently Dr Luke Massey). This amendment raised the figure to some £120,000, rising to £130,000 by 2007. It is reviewed by Trustees on a rolling basis two years ahead. A calculation of outgoings in support of the SKRC is then inputted into the Research Table.

We would similarly cost our information and support and awareness requirements; and seek to prune capital expenditure and administration to help achieve a theoretical balance of income and expenditure. Whilst the PSP Association's Headquarters were located at Wappenham, we were helped there by the low running costs of the outbuildings and by, particularly in the early stages, penny pinching in use of stationery, etc.

Once Trustees had approved our annual budget at their May Meeting, we monitored this closely against actual income and outgoings. Our Finance Committee met quarterly to compare budget with quarterly outturn and presented at biannual Trustees Meetings forecast versus outturn results. We were constantly astonished to see how near the mark these proved to be, though Peter and Gerald both agreed that luck as well as judgement played a role here, as some of the foundations of the budget were often based, for lack of anything better, on what at best could be described as hopeful assumptions.

In practice, our early budgets involved holding, as it were, a 'finger in the wind' and 'hammering it out', integrating the above approaches. Forecasting income, particularly in areas like potential legacies, can, at best, particularly early on in the life of a charity, be no more than a stab in the dark or educated guess. Our first sizeable legacy was some ten years after the Charity was formed, from Mr Megenis's estate, totalling some £500,000, coming effectively 'out of the blue'. It was this enormously generous legacy, which enabled us to purchase rather than, as then planned, rent offices, when we finally outgrew the outbuildings of the Old Rectory.

As our Charity enlarged, our budgeting became more sophisticated; and after Peter Glithero's and Gerald Kirby's arrival, more professional too! We also changed to a budget put together more and more on a bottom up basis, with each directorate producing its own 'wish list' budget to be assessed centrally and welded into the whole. As the pressure on our finances grew and with it, the need for greater transparency and additional checks and balances in the system, Tricia Holmes agreed, in addition to the other consultancy work she undertook for us, to act as Gerald's stand-in during his holidays and other necessary absences; and become, effectively, Assistant Financial Controller. We also took on a PAYE Consultant to take some of the administrative load off Gerald.

Haines Watts Financial Services had been our accountants, financial advisors and auditors since the Charity was registered and had gone some way out of their way to support us in setting up and in our early growth (apart from involving us in their fundraising go-cart day!), so it was with some reluctance, in order to reduce overheads, that we reluctantly moved from them as our auditors and accountants to Harris and Co, a smaller local Accountant, recommended by our Treasurer and approved by Trustees, since the latter could offer more of an affordable 'hands on' service at a more competitive rate.

Business planning and options for growth

One of the essential management tools for the next stage of the Charity's growth was a more sophisticated Trustee approved rolling business plan, which Peter, Gerald and I put together, drawn up based on our assessment (guided largely by the income attained in the previous years) of likely income and forecast expenditure over a five year period.

By 2001, it was clear from our work, and the resultant forecast expenditure on the horizon, that some tough decisions would need to be made on the 'Way Ahead' for the Charity. There were four main options for Trustees to consider:-

~ **Option 1.** To recognise that PSP was a comparatively rare disease and the number of people with this disease across the UK might be insufficient for a stand alone charity effectively to take on all its desired objectives. This option would mean specifically planning to remain a small charity, just providing basic information and support to those with PSP and their carers and families, though still promoting and, if possible within our budget, sponsoring key cutting edge research. This 'small charity' option is, perforce, one taken up by many of the charities supporting rare diseases.

~ **Option 2.** To seek strength in numbers by providing an umbrella group offering support not only to PSP afflicted families across the UK, but to two other closely related neurodegenerative diseases; Cortico Basal Degeneration (CBD) and Multiple System Atrophy (MSA). These two, together with Progressive Supranuclear Palsy (PSP), were sometimes referred to as the three 'ugly sisters' of Parkinson's Disease. The numbers of patients across the UK needing support from the three taken together would obviously provide a considerably greater critical mass. However, by then, Val Fleming had just set up a small charity for MSA patients called the Sarah Matheson Trust along the line of ours. He was a friend of Sarah Matheson. I first met him at our Reception, immediately after our first International Medical Workshop which he attended, whilst seeking advice from us in setting up his own charity. He and his Trustees later came to visit us and discuss the possibilities of working together. There was, however, no charity covering CBD (which was then considered to be some ten times as rare as PSP).

Under this option, we would change into one 'Umbrella Group' sheltering the three 'ugly sisters' of Parkinson's Disease, as they were then known – hence our Group, if we went for this option, would be renamed The Cinderella Group!

~ **Option 3.** To seek necessary numbers by becoming a European charity. By then we had already provided sufficient support to help establish a German PSP Group in Munich and a French Group in Brittany, both of which were, by then, moving toward becoming national charities. We were also in touch with other embryonic groups in Italy, Sweden, Switzerland, Spain, Portugal and Holland.

~ **Option 4.** To seek to continue to grow into an effective national and international charity – that is, to accept the real risk of over-extending, and go for growth as a single charity, on the assumption that the actual number of people with PSP across the UK was, as believed by many leading neurologists, far greater than then assessed (around 6.4 per 100,000 of population across the UK). There was, of course, a recognised element of risk in all the options, but definitely the greatest in Option 4.

We felt Option 1 was the easiest option, but frankly rather cowardly. It was, however, a good 'fallback' if we were to try Option 4 and fail. There would, we recognised, be problems in Option 2 in allocating research, and its cost, since PSP and MSA anyway were biologically quite distinct and different. For Option 3, there would be problems of language, registration, control and different stages of development. If however, we took up the real challenge of going for Option 4, we recognised that we could well fail. We could, of course, in that case always, in the last resort, if all went wrong, either fall back on Option 1 or, if the worst came to the worst, tail between our legs, collapse the Charity back into the Parkinson's Disease Society, which had, until we set up, provided umbrella support for those across the UK with PSP.

On Saturday, 16th February 2002, we held an extremely successful weekend 'Away Day', when the bulk of The PSP Association staff, members of our Medical Advisory Panel and Trustees met together in Slade Park Barracks in Oxford (courtesy of the Royal Rifle Volunteers and the Royal Green Jackets) to discuss these options and look, in syndicates, at the 'Way Ahead' for the Charity; and give views on the four options and key aspects of the Association's objectives in research, in support and in awareness; and the balance of expenditure between these objectives.

Although 'snap' views, perforce, had to be offered, without access to detail of income available to cover new proposals, there were some extremely helpful and constructive presentations. The very clear consensus of Trustees and Staff was in favour of going for growth as a single Charity.

This view was confirmed in a subsequent Executive Committee Meeting at which Trustees formally and unanimously selected Option 4; and agreed that the Association should accordingly seek a target annual increase in expenditure on:-

~ awareness of 20%

~ information and support of 15%

~ research of 10%

~ and administration of not more than 5%

over the next five years. The Association was to construct a new five year business plan accordingly for Trustee approval. This would provide key guidance for the future growth of the Charity.

The emphasis on awareness reflected our view that, particularly amongst relevant health and welfare professionals, this was the key to success for The PSP Association, measured in terms of care and support provided to afflicted families and the level of funding by Government for research into PSP as well as numbers joining the Association.

Our five year plan was duly produced, approved and subsequently updated annually over its fixed period (and duly, in turn, replaced by later models) over the next ten years, the latest Trustee approved plan covering the period 2007/09 to 2011/12).

Two years after our Away Day, our 2003 Joint International Medical Workshop at Stowe focussed on the clinical, pathological and biological commonalities between PSP, CBD and MSA. There were very clear differences between PSP and MSA, with the latter perhaps being closer to Parkinson's Disease. However, in comparing PSP and the rarer CBD, a few scientists at this Workshop considered CBD was no more than just a variant of PSP – or vice versa. Others felt the two were very closely related, with much in common, but we were very aware that CBD had no patient group of its own.

By then, following our decision to go for growth as a single disease Charity, such growth had been more than assured. However, because of the scientific views expressed about PSP and CBD, we revisited the possibilities of a 'revised' Option 2; that is, widening our umbrella to include patients with Cortico Basal Degeneration and their families.

At our next Meeting, Trustees agreed to a policy of 'opening our doors' to patients, carers and families with CBD. Accordingly, we rewrote our leaflets and adjusted the workload of the Charity to become as inclusive as possible for CBD afflicted families. Whenever we now refer to PSP, we mean both PSP and CBD unless we state otherwise (e.g. when comparing symptoms).

As the Charity grew, so inevitably did our costs. Whilst we remained in the outbuildings of the Old Rectory, the Koe Family waived any rent there, a useful saving in core costs; but over the next few years, the number of our employees and consultants steadily grew, putting pressure not only on space available, but on costs. Salaries and fees were, of course, allocated in our budgeting by areas of work, but administrative expenditure still inevitably grew; as did office expenditure in terms of IT, photocopying and office materials. With the move into our new offices, the need to take on a part time office manager and the cost of essential work in repairs and maintenance meant this figure rising to nearer ten percent but still comparatively low, set against our peers.

Core funding for charities has always been harder to acquire than funding for a particular project or for sponsorship of a particular piece of research, where Donor Trusts are more likely to respond positively, particularly to a well presented appeal within their area of interest. Core costs therefore tend to come out of income brought in through subscriptions, interest on investments and/or from events run by the charity or in which the charity partakes. The one off immensely generous contribution from the October Club made a huge difference here both in the research we could take on and in covering some of our core costs to enable us to take on more staff and grow into a medium sized charity.

Company law requires Trustees to prepare accounts for each financial year, which give a true and fair view of the state of affairs of the charity and its incoming resources and application of resources, including its net income and expenditure for the year.

In preparing such accounts, Trustees are required to select suitable accounting policies and then apply them consistently, make judgements and estimates that are reasonable and prudent and prepare the accounts on an ongoing, basis unless it is inappropriate to presume that the charity will continue in operation. Our job within The PSP Association was to make absolutely sure that it remained appropriate.

The process started each year in close liaison with our Accountants. The contents of Report and Accounts for Companies are laid down in the Companies Act and, for charities which are also Companies limited by Guarantee, by both the Charity Commissioners and Companies Act, under UK General Auditing and Accounting Procedures (GAAP) and Statement of Operating and Reporting Procedures (SORP). SORP 2005 introduces all UK GAAP standards issued up to, and inclusive of, 2004.

The Report, for example, must include the following:-

~   Structure, Governance and Management
~   Objectives and Activities
~   Achievements and Performance
~   Financial Review
~   Risk Assessment Statement
~   Plans for Future Periods

SORP cites in some detail the required contents of a charity's Annual Report, including administrative information, (such as the charity name, address, registration number, names of Trustees, etc), structure, governance and management (including the appointment and training of Trustees), objectives and activities (a summary of objectives as set out in its governing document and main activities in relation to these objectives), achievements and performance, (a summary of achievements over the year) a financial review (including policy on reserves) and funds held (effectively a description of assets and who holds them).

Report and Accounts offer a real opportunity for charities to inform a wide audience about what they are doing and why. We have, since our first Report and Accounts, consistently used this opportunity to 'spread the word' about PSP, about afflicted families and our concerns about the support they receive within the NHS at home, in hospital and in nursing and care homes; and about our Charity and its work – what we are doing and why, in a full and detailed report, covering not only information required by SORP, but a wider account of the Charity's objectives and progress toward them.

We therefore aimed from the start to 'set out our stall', including in our Report everything required by SORP, but going a great deal further. In addition to required SORP paragraphs, our Chairman's Statement majors on risk assessment and future plans, the Chief Executive's Report on the history of the Association, on its detailed progress over the year by objectives against our Trustee approved Five Year Business Plan; and on its planned progress within each objective for the forthcoming year, and the Treasurer's Report covers Trustees' responsibilities and auditors comments.

This process is painstaking and time consuming, but the discipline of this annual review enables us to correct deviations and plan ahead by comparing outcome with forecast and Business Plan objectives and move forward into the next year with greater confidence.

The production of the Report and Accounts (R & A) requires, as would be expected, careful forward planning. At the end of the process, the final draft of the Report and Accounts need to be 'received' by Trustees at their November Meeting immediately prior to the Annual General Meeting at which the R & A are approved prior to despatch to Companies House and the Charity Commissioners.

Working back in time, the process starts in the run-up to 30th June each year, being the last day of the Charity's accounting period, with a draft of the Report being put together under the Chief Executive's broad direction. During this phase, Gerald would work closely with Harris & Co in providing necessary paperwork and coordinating the production of the draft Accounts, which would inform the Report Section. These two parts of the report needed to be assembled separately, then married up. During this period, our Treasurer (Peter Glithero), our Financial Controller (Gerald Kirby), and myself as Chief Executive met regularly, both informally and formally over the period, to coordinate input.

Before being 'received' by Trustees, the married up draft Report and Accounts needed to be reviewed and signed off by our Executive Sub Committee, following which our Accountants then signed off, as auditors.

In summary, around thirty five percent of our income has gone into research, some twenty five percent into information and support, some eighteen percent into awareness, some fifteen percent into 'seed corn' fundraising and some seven percent on administration. Although these figures have varied by up to five percent each way over the years and administration has grown from five to nearer ten percent, the proportion has broadly been steady over the life of the Charity. In all, we have to date spent some £2 million pounds on research.

The PSP Association annual income grew steadily from 1994 to some £450,000 in 2004. Then, thank to the magnificent contribution from the October Club and subsequent Megenis legacy, rose sharply over the next two years. From 2006, it has continued to grow some 10% per year and by the end 2007 reached an annual income of some £800,000. In 2008, the Charity is seeking to raise one million pounds. It's current assets are some £1,400,000 of which some £600,000 is reflected in its Offices in Towcester. We have no mortgage on this valuable freehold property, which includes a car park that can accommodate – albeit at a squeeze – all the cars of The PSP Association staff who work there.

As the Charity continues to grow, new initiatives are being taken forward by Jane Hardy, including greater emphasis on budgetary control of directorates by Directors, a move to accruals accounting (with updated charity accounting software), and increasing financial performance monitoring with the Financial Sub Committee reporting more regularly to Trustees. Consideration is also being given to adjusting our Financial Year to align with the tax year. All this is good. As a medium sized charity working in a more regulated environment, the growing need for greater professionalism in financial accounting is undisputable.

9. *Conclusions*

It was not until the second half of the twentieth century that illnesses relating to the brain were sufficiently well understood by the medical profession for public attitudes significantly to change from the social stigma of being given such a diagnosis. Re-reading *Jane Eyre* sharply reminds one of the public's attitude to those with brain diseases; attitudes which could lead to institutionalisation of the patient and ostracism by society of their family. Even in recent times children talked about 'the looney bin' and being put in the 'mad house'.

Today, a number of neurological diseases are now known to be caused by no more than perhaps the change of one letter in the genetic coding in chromosomes handed down by parents. Unfortunately, such changes have the potential – sometimes on their own and sometimes combined with an environmental trigger – to damage the astonishingly complex working and 'electronic wiring' of the brain, in turn leading to the loss of key functions and capabilities.

The biology leading to neurodegenerative diseases is now pretty well understood and for the better known of these, such as Alzheimer's Disease and Parkinson's Disease, there is sufficient knowledge of their mechanisms and consequent focussed research to give a real promise of treatment and even cure over the next decade. Controversial techniques involving stem cells and cloning are very much in the news today and, in time, may lead to successful treatment of the above.

The less common of these brain diseases still remain little known by the public at large, though within the relevant international medical and scientific community, there are highly dedicated groups working to exploit disease mechanisms to find treatment and cure. PSP is one of the more prevalent of these.

Looking back in time, in a more personal way, I remember as yesterday, Sara cheerfully and energetically pushing a wheelbarrow full of sand beside our outbuildings at Gayton and the crack of her head hitting a sharp extension of scaffolding. Was this the trigger which set off this disease for her and the consequent events which led to her death?

The jury is still 'out' on whether a blow like this can cause such a disease, though 'pugilistic parkinsonism' (essentially the name given to effect over time of punches accelerating the brain's 'soft' interior against the containing framework of bone) and its link to Parkinson's Disease provides strong evidence that it can.

In Sara's case, her subsequent difficult-to-define symptoms, dislike of bright light and fear of falling, gradually but inexorably progressed over the next year to a firm diagnosis of PSP at the National Hospital for Neurology. After some three years courageously fighting this disease, she died in January 1995, but not before, through frustration and even anger over its apparent neglect by the medical profession, we had together registered and started up The PSP Association.

Some fourteen years later, our Charity has made, thanks to overwhelming and generous support from people across the world, impressive progress towards its objectives in research, in support and in engendering awareness of PSP, though there is still much to be done.

This is a personal story largely about the setting up and growth of our Charity to help people with this particular neurodegenerative disease and their carers; and to seek to redress the unacceptable inequalities in care and treatment they receive. Thanks to the enormously generous support from families afflicted by this disease, from philanthropic organisations and from many different and often quite unexpected sources, we have established the necessary funding to start and grow a capable organisation. But yet more support will be needed fully to achieve our goals.

For there is still no known treatment and no cure for this disease. Its cause is still unknown. There is also no diagnostic marker yet available to assist the clinician in the often difficult differential diagnosis which, if disease-moderating drugs become available, will need to be much sooner after onset. At present, even with the best neurologist, diagnosis is still often some three or four years into the disease and still remains dependent on the judgement and skill of the clinician, who is doing well to achieve, against the 'gold standard' of pathological diagnosis, a ninety percent success rate.

Because of its historic links with Parkinson's Disease and its ability to mimic the latter's symptoms, PSP has continued to remain tucked away as a form of parkinsonism, despite recent research, which confirms it to be a quite distinct and different disease. As it emerges from the shadow of Parkinson's Disease, recent research has shown it to be at least as common – and most neurologists would agree at least as nasty – as its far better known cousin Motor Neurone Disease.

When asked what the initials PSP stand for, the average 'person on the street' is still more likely to say 'Play Station Portable' than 'Progressive Supranuclear Palsy'. Until there is far greater public understanding of such diseases and consequent support for them, there is unlikely to be the political will to fund the necessary care for sufferers and for the urgently required further research and clinical trials to find effective treatments and cure.

Meanwhile, there remains across the UK an acute shortage of neurologists, nurses and therapists with specialist knowledge in the less common and less well known neurodegenerative diseases. Although we are no longer near the bottom of the European table in such statistics, the shortage needs addressing urgently so that the Quality Requirements laid down in the National Service Framework for Neurological Conditions can be met.

The care and support provided by the NHS and by Nursing and Care homes remains patchy across the UK, still with dreadful examples of neglect and a heavy financial burden on afflicted families, who themselves provide the bulk of necessary care.

The cost to the public purse in care provided by the NHS for those with neurological conditions, even though often heavily subsidised by voluntary support, is still substantial. A figure of £200,000 a year is quoted for a Motor Neurone Disease patient in the end stages of this disease; and PSP is unlikely to be any less.

There are, today, some 10 million people with neurological conditions in the UK of which up to some 10,000 are believed to have PSP, whose average lifespan will be some seven years from onset of the disease. During this time, the disease will progressively strip them of many of those capabilities that make life worth living, leaving the intellect largely intact whilst trapped in a useless body. Without easy access to palliative care in the later stages of this disease, desperate people with progressive diseases like PSP may still opt to go to Switzerland for euthanasia.

The balance of effort between Voluntary Organisations, such as ours, funded by the generosity of the public, as against that provided through the National Health System remains a controversial and topical debate. It is relevant therefore to reflect on what we, as a charity, have done with the money that we have been given and the funds we have generated.

We have funded some £2 million of carefully selected, cutting-edge research. And we have pump-primed at least three times that amount, working closely with CurePSP, our US sister charity. CurePSP have in turn invested a similar amount to us and pump primed the US National Institutes of Health (NIS) and its National Institute of Neurological Diseases and Strokes (NINDS) into several million dollars worth of research into PSP. Progress in basic and transitional research into PSP has come a long way since 1994. We are now starting clinical trials into possible disease-moderating drugs. Funding for such research is no longer left solely to charities such as ours, but is now supported by governments across the USA and Europe. And we hope soon that this will be backed by pharmaceutical companies, who have been understandably reluctant to invest in less common diseases that are unlikely to generate a suitable return on their investment. Incentives, both in Europe and in the USA, are now in place to encourage them to do so.

Meanwhile, thanks to research we have sponsored, powerful MRI scanners and more sophisticated techniques for analysing spinal fluid are already providing supporting evidence for differential clinical diagnosis in PSP and an effective means of measuring the effects of drugs on the progress of the disease. They show promise too of providing much needed diagnostic markers. Although the cause is still questioned, the mechanism of PSP is much better understood and treatment to slow or even stop this disease is a realistic possibility in the not too distant future.

The PSP Association's Nurse Specialists and their 24 hour, seven day a week dedicated telephone counselling service lies at the heart of our Charity's work. They handle between them many, often distressed, evening calls or concerns from patients or their carers. They attend neurology clinics in London, Cambridge, Newcastle and Cardiff and know many of the relevant professionals within and outside their areas of responsibility. Together with our Local Support Groups, which now cover the whole of the UK, they provide an essential additional support for patients and carers, not available through the NHS.

The comprehensive Professionals and Carers Information Packs we put out, together with other literature and videos such as *A Physician's Guide to PSP* have not only directly helped inform and support people with PSP, their carers and their families; they have also raised awareness of this disease amongst relevant health and welfare professionals across Europe, so helping them to provide more of the care so desperately needed.

The work of our Development Officers in their areas and the Regional Information Seminars they organise have also not only had a considerable impact on professional awareness of this disease, but strengthened the direct support we can provide to patients and carers within these regions. They are being linked in with the new Regional Neurological Alliances across England. Our 'top down' awareness campaign addressing relevant umbrella groups in this field has also drip fed greater understanding of the prevalence and devastating consequences of PSP.

As awareness of PSP grows both within the relevant health and welfare professionals and amongst the general public at large, so attitudes are starting to change.

At the beginning, thanks to the immense generosity of our friends and relatives, of patients and their carers and of their families and friends, The PSP Association grew to a point where wider support 'kicked in'.

This same group of people have continued faithfully to support our fundraising in many different ways, particularly in terms of events we have run and taken part in. The places we have obtained in marathons (for example, through our Flora London Marathon Golden Bonds) have been taken up largely by those who have seen first hand the effects of this devastating disease.

I have been both humbled and inspired by the support we have been given and by the courage of those touched by this dreadful disease.

I would like, too, to particularly mention the tremendous contribution made by an immensely focussed group of scientists across the world, who have dedicated their lives to understanding the mechanisms of the brain and to finding treatments and cure for these horrific neurodegenerative diseases. They have given hope to those now struggling with their inexorable progression. Through the close coordination of their work, astonishing progress has been made in basic, transitional and clinical research into this particular brain disease. There is now some light at the end of the tunnel.

Three crucial events have combined to 'supercharge' the Association's growth; **firstly**, Dudley Moore's courageous announcement to the World in 1999 that he had PSP; **secondly**, the immensely generous and powerful October Club selecting us as their Charity of the Year in 2004; **and thirdly**, the support we have received from our hierarchy; from Her Royal Highness, The Duchess of Gloucester GCVO, as our Patron, from The Lord Bramall and The Lord Guthrie as our first and second Presidents, from The Lord Coe and Professor Blakemore as our Vice Presidents and from The Lord Naseby and Sir Michael Carleton-Smith as our first and second Chairman.

Without their wholehearted and generous support, the growth we have achieved would have been impossible. We owe all of them a real debt of gratitude. Lord Coe's support for the Charity both before and after his mother's diagnosis of having PSP, and her subsequent death from this fatal disease, has been invaluable and a major fundraiser; as has been the Major Fundraising Appeals Committee he has chaired.

The generosity of such people, of Donor Trusts, of Corporates and of individual members of the public, once they become aware of such need, has been both moving and inspiring. Their contributions have enabled The PSP Association to move forward toward its objectives in the provision of information and support, in research and in awareness building to enable it to have its goal in sight – clinical trials to seek treatment and cure for this devastating disease.

Finally, I would like to thank our dedicated and loyal PSP Office Team, who have shown patience, generosity and determination and at times much needed humour to cope as a close knit group and take our Charity forward toward its objectives; and my successor, Jane Hardy, in the wonderful way she has furthered progress in work still to be done. Some of the new initiatives I refer to are hers and already she is taking the Charity to its next peak at noteworthy speed – the summit is in sight or, using a different metaphor, there is definite light at the end of the tunnel! We have been extremely fortunate to find her to carry the baton forward.

Painfully slowly, awareness of this disease and its effect on afflicted families has steadily risen over the last fifteen years, amongst the general public. We have still some way to go before PSP is as well recognised as Motor Neurone Disease but, looking back over our Charity's lifespan and its work to date, we recall those evocative lines from Arthur Clough's poem:

> "For while the tired waves, vainly breaking, seem here no painful inch to gain,
> Far back, through creeks and inlets making, comes silent, flooding in, the main.
> And not by eastern windows only, when daylight comes, comes in the light,
> In front, the sun climbs slow, how slowly, but westward, look, the land is bright."[22]

This Book has been written in loving memory of Sara and all those who have suffered and died from this brutal disease; and those who cared for them, as their PSP inexorably progressed.

---

22. *Arthur Hugh Clough*